Table of Contents

♡ The recipes in this book do not contain preservatives – to ensure freshness add a frozen, freezer pack to lunches.

♡ Recipes have been tested in U.S. Standard measurements. Common metric measurements are given as a convenience for those who are more familiar with metric. Recipes have not been tested in metric.

Wheat Allergies: If you have a wheat allergy or want to use a different type of flour; all of the recipes in this book can be used interchangeably with spelt, barley or oat flours.

Coconut Oil: In the cookie or loaf recipes where butter is being used, you can substitute coconut oil, if you choose. It adds a nice flavor.

Introduction

The reason I wrote this book was because when I spoke to other mothers their major complaint was always the same; "What do you put in your kids lunches?" I remember when I was a kid having a very boring lunch. It was too healthy and uninspired and I felt like I never had a treat. I wanted to be able to bridge the gap between healthy and tasty. It seems like things either taste great and are bad for you or are good for you and taste like a bale of hay, and never the twain shall meet.

When I had kids of my own, I realized that what I did from the start could affect them later on in life, and that felt like a huge responsibility. I have watched too many people I love die of cancer and other degenerative diseases. I have also watched too many people young and old suffer the health problems from obesity; I myself was one of those people. I was a fat kid and fought a weight problem my whole life. I did not want to set my kids up for the same future, so I vowed to show them something different.

Kid's taste buds today are fried! Deep-fried that is! They are numbed from the salt and fat in most processed foods. We have an epidemic on our hands and children are the ones who are going to pay the price from our laziness in not feeding them real whole foods from scratch. I know that boxed, pre-packaged food looks so good in the picture and looks so easy – but in the end, is it worth it? We seem to be giving our kids a mixed message. On one hand, we tell them they need to get exercise and eat healthy and then we get lazy and feed them garbage because it appears to be the easier solution. If we really want our kids to be healthy and energetic, we need to fuel their bodies with real food that will give them energy and keep them healthy.

We live in a very fast-paced world and we all are short on time, but really the time it takes to make a single recipe is about 35-45 minutes maximum. I tend to take a day and make it my baking day and go crazy and double recipes and freeze, freeze, freeze. Then in the mornings I send the kids downstairs to pick whatever they want in their lunch that day. I have a friend who bakes one thing twice or three times a week, that way she

LUNCHBOX
LOVE

by
Sally King

Over 60 Delicious and Healthy Lunch Recipes Your Kids will LOVE

Lunchbox Love
by
Sally King

First Printing - August, 2008

Copyright @ 2008 by
D-K Publishing
#5, 26106 Twp Road, 532 A
Spruce Grove, AB, T7Y 1A3
Telephone: 780-418-2266
E-mail: ms-king@hotmail.com   www.lunchboxlove.ca

Library and Archives Canada Cataloguing in Publication

King, Sally, 1964-
    Lunchbox love : Over 60 delicious and healthy lunch recipes your kids will love / Sally King

Includes index.
ISBN: 978-1-897010-47-1

    1. Lunchbox cookery. I. Title.

TX735.K55 2008   641.5'34   C2008-904563-7

Photography by:Susan Barker

Cover Design by:
Brian Danchuk, Brian Danchuk Design, Regina, Saskatchewan

Page Design, formatting and index by:
Iona Glabus, Centax Books

Designed, Printed and Produced in Canada by:
Centax Books, a division of PrintWest Communications Ltd.
Publishing Director: Dan Marce
1150 Eighth Avenue, Regina, Saskatchewan, Canada S4R 1C9
(306) 525-2304   FAX (306) 757-2439
E-mail: centax@printwest.com   www.centaxbooks.com

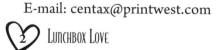

always has baking on hand. When it comes to the cabbage buns, calzones, pasties, and samosas; I make the fillings one day, the dough and assembly the next day, so that it is not such a daunting job all at once. To have chicken for wrap fillings, I will grill enough chicken breasts for a couple of days and use what I need. Simply having a plan and food in the freezer is a huge time saver. The key is getting organized and having the ingredients on hand, so that if a spare window presents itself you have all the necessary ingredients to whip something up in a hurry.

This process is a journey, I did not flip on a switch one day and suddenly we ate everything healthy and organic. I do not expect you to either. When I look back at some of the things that I fed my kids unknowingly – I cringe. I made a decision then to not look back. I chose to live by the phrase I heard on Oprah, and that is, "When you know better, you do better" and that is how I live my life and that is maybe something you can also adopt. We all want the best for our kids and we all do the best we can, so sit back, thumb through this cookbook and try something different – you never know you just might like it, and best of all so will your kids!

Sally

....

Note: My recipes purposely do not have nutritional analysis, because I feel we are a society obsessed with fat and calories. Very few have lost weight long-term by eating low-fat and low-calorie. My recipes contain good-fat and are extremely nutrient dense. This is what all kids need – not trans-fats and empty calories. They need REAL food made with LOVE!

If you require nutritional analysis you can find it on
my website: **www.lunchboxlove.ca**

Dedication

To Brady & Tyson, my reason for why I do everything.

To our daughter, this book kept me busy while we waited for you.

To Murray, the best sous chef a girl could ever want.

Acknowledgements

Where do I start? How can I possibly thank everyone who helped me put this book together? I am so blessed – to have so many wonderful and supportive friends. I want to thank Bernie Defreitas who helped me immeasurably – truly my computer genius and a wonderful friend! Sue Browning, with her wealth of great suggestions that I always value. Pam Hirtle, for her constant encouragement, telling me that this was right thing to do. Carmen, Maxine and Sandra, for recipe testing and endorsements. Thank you to Dr. James Wiedrick for taking time out of his busy schedule to write the foreword. Kim Marchuk, you have changed my life and taught me so much. I could not have pulled this off without ALL of you.

Thank you also to Brady, Tyson and Murray, who didn't just eat the successes, but also the flops! I am a very lucky girl!

Foreword

"As a family physician, I recognize that the youth of today have many obstacles to good health; fewer natural opportunities for physical fitness, an abundance of exposure to television/computer/video game products, and an excess of junk food. Childhood obesity is rampant. The medical community is now recognizing the potential tidal wave of diseases, such as early onset Type 2 Diabetes and cardiovascular complications that are the natural result of those problems.

Parents and educators need to purposefully take steps to lead our youth down the path to health. Children need us to be role models for active living. They need to be provided with healthy dietary choices. They also need to be shown that good nutrition is fun, tasty and essential for properly fuelling their bodies.

Lunchbox Love is all about properly preparing our kids for their day. I applaud Sally for her work in compiling great recipes that have kid appeal. A collection like this is one tool in the overall health strategy for our next generation. Enjoy!"

– **James Wiedrick**, MD CCFP

....

"As a nutritionist, I am always seeking out recipes for my clients, unique nutritional needs. I also realize that in today's fast-paced world, recipes need to be enjoyable and easy to prepare. *Lunchbox Love* is a way for parents to create a variety of easy, yet nutritious, fun meals their children will enjoy. My hope is that the information found in this book will inspire many families to create less of a gap between the comfort of home cooking and the comfort they feel while being nourished."

– **Kim Marchuk**, NCP, QBS – Holistic Nutritionist

How to Introduce Kids to New Foods

Now that you have bought this book, you cannot suddenly change your child's diet and expect them not to rebel. I know adult men and women who claim they do not like onions probably because when they were a child they told their mother they didn't like them and so their mother stopped cooking with them. I know I am probably going to hell for all the lies I have told my kids over the years. When my oldest was about 3, he said he didn't like red pepper, I said "Good, because this is red star fruit." He was 8, before he realized that they were red peppers. My little guy told me he didn't like raw onions, because they were too spicy. I told him I sautéed them just for his salad – he eats them now with no problems. It is all how you sell it. My kids have eaten this way most of their lives, but if you are going to make some changes in your child's diet then do it gradually. Here are a few tips that I found work.

If you have an onion hater, chop them up small in a food processor and chances are good they will not even notice them.

When my kids decide they do not like something I will find a way to incorporate that food into other things and break it in slowly. My son, Brady, used to love avocado and then one day he got a bad piece and he gagged and said he never wanted avocado again. I found ways to hide it. He now loves guacamole, so I make it often as a veggie dip and in wraps and sandwiches. Avocado has a subtle taste, and that is how the avocado chocolate pudding came about. It was a way of getting great, healthy fat into his diet without him knowing about it.

If your child is new to whole-wheat flour, start out gradually. Do not jump in with both feet all at once. Start out with half-and-half and work your way up, that way your kids will not notice and whatever you do, do not tell them.

The way to get kids to eat salads is to make them interesting and flavorful. Add nuts, seeds, dried cranberries, mandarin oranges or avocado. Remember the darker the lettuce the more nutrients and the more flavor.

Really the key to changing your child's diet is to persevere and be patient and to keep introducing new things. It can take 10-20 tries for your child to get used to something different. Most importantly remember, no child in the history of the world has ever voluntarily starved themselves to death, because they didn't like what was being offered – so do not give in. They will not die!

Lunch Packing Tips:

♡ **Garbage Free Lunches**: It has been estimated that on average a school-age child using disposable lunches, generates 67 pounds of waste per school year. That equates to 18,760 pounds of lunch waste for just one average-size elementary school. Stop using sealable plastic bags and start using reusable containers. Forget individually pre-packed products and make your own healthier alternatives. Every little bit counts!

♡ Garbageless lunches are cheaper because you are not paying for all the packaging.

♡ Use an insulated lunch bag to keep food at the correct temperature.

♡ To keep lunches cold, place a freezer pack in the lunch bag. Add cold, refrigerated items.

♡ For hot food items, purchase a thermos container and preheat it by pouring boiling water inside. Let it sit for a couple of minutes before dumping out and pour in the hot food.

♡ I personally recommend using a stainless-steel thermos container over heating food in the microwave. You will be heating things in plastic containers and the chemicals from the plastic will leach into the food.

♡ Purchase an inexpensive set of stainless steel cutlery at a discount store to send only with lunches. This will prevent plastic cutlery from ending up in the landfills and if they lose a cheap set, your home set is still complete.

♡ Send cloth napkins; again, go to a discount store or garage sales and pick up inexpensive napkins and wash them. They don't have to be fine linen, just enough to wipe their hands. Paper napkins, again kill trees and end up in the landfill.

♡ Buy a large selection of reusable containers in small sizes.

♡ Buy bigger containers of yogurt, cottage cheese, etc. and transfer them into small reusable containers. Do not buy items in single serving sizes; it just creates more garbage to fill up our landfills.

♡ Wash containers every night in hot, soapy water. Do not put them in the dishwasher, it is too hot and may break down the plastic and cause leaching.

♡ Purchase a little salt shaker, fill it with sea salt and send it along for salting tomatoes or boiled eggs.

♡ I ask my kids to bring home any peels and vegetable waste. We compost them to prevent filling up the landfill.

♡ To prevent sandwiches from becoming soggy, send tomatoes or pickles, separately in a reusable containers. The children can add it to the sandwich at school.

♡ Place softer fruit in reusable plastic containers to prevent bruising.

♡ I peel oranges and kiwis for my kids so that they do not have to do it; then store it in a plastic container. They also have the tendency to eat the fruit if it is already cut-up.

♡ My boys are at the tooth-losing stage and cannot bite a whole apple because their front teeth are loose; so I cut the apple and remove the core. When you store apples in a sealed container, they do not go brown.

♡ I send ice water in a stainless steel water bottle for my kids. I stay away from juices as they have a lot of sugar and we have a nation of dehydrated people. Fruit juices also do not have the fibre that eating the actual fruit does. I may send a juice box as a special treat 3-4 times a year but always a real fruit juice nothing from a concentrate.

♡ Vary lunches everyday so that your children do not get bored and want to head for the vending machines or corner store. It is all about making it interesting.

....

"What great healthy, alternatives to those over-processed, convenience lunch items on the market today. I think you'd have pretty envious kids in the lunch room and a whole generation of healthier, more energetic kids outperforming old standards".

– **Jan Marce**, mother and retired school administrator

Who Knew ...

Children DO need fat for proper growth and development; but the fat needs to be good fats not saturated or trans fats. Some good choices are nuts, seeds, avocados, eggs (Omega-3 even better). You can also supplement with flavored fish oils. I give my kids 1 tsp. (5 mL) orange-flavored fish oil, which doesn't have a fishy taste.

A poor diet can cause constipation, gall stones, bloating, gas and bad breath ... junk food anyone?

Sleep deprivation is a real problem for many children. Common side effects are depression, negative self image, poor coping skills and behavioral problems at home and school. One study showed that "A" Students get 20 minutes more sleep and go to bed on average 40 minutes earlier then students who have lower grades. ADHD has also been associated with insufficient sleep.

Obesity Rates in Children: Did you know that in 1978, 3% of the children in Canada were obese. In 2004, 8% (estimated 500,000) of Canadian children were obese. This means that the rates have more than doubled. In adults the growth in obesity is even higher. The American rates over the past thirty years have more than doubled for kids aged 2-5 and 12-19 and more than tripled for children aged 6-11 years. Approximately nine million children over 6 years of age are considered obese in the United States. Don't set your kids up for failure, take the time to show them that not only does healthy food taste good, it's easy to prepare as well! Why is it that so many of parents are becoming more and more aware of the foods and choices we are making for ourselves but still feeding our children processed foods and non-nutritional garbage? It should also be noted that just because your kids are not overweight, this shouldn't be used as an indicator of your child's health. Think about the nutrition that's going into their bodies and ask yourself if you're making the best choices for them. Also, children who are obese have a much higher rate of depression.

Why Choose Organics? I choose to feed my kids organic food mainly because of no pesticides, no herbicides, higher nutritional content and sustainable farming is better for the earth. No matter what anyone argues, the tomatoes that I buy from my local farmer at the farmer's market, taste 5,000 times better than the often tasteless ones that are available in grocery stores. I'm not telling you that you have to go organic, this is a personal choice that my family has made, but do take the time to look into it.

 12 Lunchbox Love

The Dirty Dozen: If you're not ready to go 100% organic, here is a list of twelve types of produce that you should really try to buy organic if they are available. These items are conventionally the biggest offenders for containing and or using the most pesticides and chemicals.

- Apples
- Bell Peppers
- Celery
- Cherries
- Imported Grapes
- Nectarines

- Peaches
- Pears
- Potatoes
- Red Raspberries
- Spinach
- Strawberries

Pesticides: Due to the size of kids bodies, they can quickly reach toxicity from pesticide levels said to be safe by the FDA. The EPA claims that pesticides only pose a "negligible risk" to health.

"This 'negligible risk' standard fails to recognize that, by definition, any exposure to a poison is too much. Poisons are cumulative. Obviously, poisons are in greater concentrated proportion to children than adults, to women than men. Often, the combination of poisons is even more deadly than the action of a poison on its own." – Empty Harvest by Dr. Bernard Jensen and Mark Anderson

Juice: Some interesting facts on brand name juice drinks:

Product	Teaspoons of Sugar per 355 mL
Cola	10 teaspoons
Sunny Delight	10.5 teaspoons
V-8 Splash	10.5 teaspoons
Five Alive	10 teaspoons
Fruitopia	9.5 teaspoons
Nestea	6 teaspoons
Powerade	6 teaspoons
Water	0 teaspoons

Filling your kids up with juice, means they have less room for healthier foods. Too much juice can also cause tooth decay and diarrhea. Check labels if you buy fruit juice – just because it contains real fruit juice doesn't mean that's the only thing in it. Water is always your best choice for quenching thirst and hydration.

Type 2 Diabetes and High Blood Pressure: Along with the huge increase in childhood obesity comes a huge increase in Type 2 Diabetes and high blood pressure. Kids are becoming more sedentary and eating more junk food than ever before. This dangerous combination leads to small children developing "adult" conditions such as high blood pressure and high cholesterol levels. Lets face it, there are only a limited amount of years we as parents have to actually choose what goes into our children's bodies. As they get older, earn their own money and move away from home they will be making their own choices of what to feed themselves. When they are young is when we should introduce them to different choices, tastes, and the benefits of real food.

High Fructose Corn Syrup: High fructose corn syrup is a sweetener that is used in most processed foods. It is extremely cheap to make, spoil resistant and super sweet. It is consumed in great quantities.

Research shows that fructose promotes disease more than other sugars. For example, every cell in your body metabolizes glucose but only the liver metabolizes fructose. Animals fed high fructose diets develop fatty liver deposits and cirrhosis, similar to the livers of alcoholics.

There has been studies done that say the increased use of processed foods with high fructose corn syrup directly parallels the huge rise in diabetes and obesity.

HFCS's are found in a majority of products including pop, cereals, granola bars, juices and even some yogurts. They are found in many other products not mentioned here. So buyer beware!

Plastic Water Bottles: Plastics made from polycarbonate resin can leach bisphenol-A (BPA). BPA is a very dangerous hormone disruptor. It may impair reproductive organs and effect tumors, breast tissue development and prostate development. The BPA leaches into the water and increases with exposure to heat and cleaning agents – think dishwasher. The perfect solution is to use a stainless steel water bottle, but make sure that it is stainless steel both inside and out. They are great because they can hold both hot and cold liquids. One great water bottle I would recommend is called the Klean Kanteen available in different sizes.

LUNCHBOX LOVE

DIPS & SPREADS

Speedy Guacamole

This is a super fast dip for veggies or on wraps.

1	avocado	1
2 tbsp.	salsa	30 mL
1-2	garlic cloves	1-2
2 tsp.	lime or lemon juice	10 mL
¼ tsp.	chili powder	1 mL
dash	sea salt	dash

♡ Put everything in a food processor and blend until very smooth.

....

Lunchbox Tip: Make this in the morning, it will stay fresh until lunch time.

Avocados are an amazing source of nutrition. They have nearly 20 vitamins, minerals and beneficial plant compounds. They contain the carotenoid lutein that helps to maintain healthy eyes. Avocados have something called beta-sitosterol in which helps to maintain healthy cholesterol levels. They are a great source of healthy fats that keep kids brains growing and healthy. Avocados are a great source of vitamin E as well and they are filling, tasty and great for you.

Yield: 3 servings or
     approximately
     ¾ cup (175 mL)
Prep Time: 5 minutes

Tzaziki

A cool, refreshing dip for veggies or on wraps or with chicken- or beef-on-a-stick.

1	English cucumber	1
1-2	garlic cloves, minced	1-2
1 cup	sour cream	250 mL
2 tbsp.	plain yogurt	30 mL
2 tbsp.	whole milk	30 mL
½ tsp.	oregano	2 mL
	sea salt & pepper	

♡ Grate cucumber with skin left on, into a sieve or colander. Press the cucumber into the sieve/colander to remove excess water.

♡ Combine garlic, sour cream, oregano, sea salt and pepper in a bowl. Stir in the cucumber.

Who Knew?

Yogurt: Not all yogurts are the made alike. Make sure when buying yogurt that it has the active live bacteria in it which promotes good stomach flora. Lots of commercial yogurts are loaded with sugar and added chemicals. I buy plain, organic yogurt and add my own fruit. If it needs sweetening, I use maple syrup.

Yield: 6 servings or approx. 3 cups (750 mL)
Prep Time: 10 minute

Hummus

This is great in your kids lunches instead of a sandwich. Serve with pita bread and veggies for dipping – sorry about the garlic breath.

19 oz.	can chickpeas	284 g
2-3	garlic cloves	2-3
2 tbsp.	tahini	30 mL
1 tbsp.	olive oil	15 mL
2 tbsp.	plain yogurt	30 mL
1 tbsp.	lemon juice	15 mL
¼ tsp.	cumin	1 mL
	sea salt & pepper	

♡ Blend all ingredients, in a food processor, until very smooth.

Chickpeas

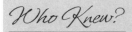

Chickpeas: Did you know that chickpeas are very high in dietary fiber and protein? They are also an excellent source of zinc and folate. Folate is necessary for maintaining and producing new cells. I always keep a can of chickpeas stocked in the cupboard.

Yield: 8 servings or
    approximately
    2 cups (500 mL)
Prep Time: 10 minutes

My Favorite Pesto

This is my healthy, last-minute standby when, "Oh my gosh, what am I going to put in the kids lunches?" I pull a couple of cubes of prepared pesto out of the freezer. While the pesto is thawing, I cook some whole-wheat pasta (whatever you have on hand) usually penne. When the pasta is cooked and drained, I often add fresh tomatoes, cucumbers and frozen peas or corn; stir the pesto into the pasta; place in a thermos container and "voila," lunch is done! Couldn't be easier. In a wrap, pesto can replace the mayonnaise.

⅓ cup	pine nuts, toasted	75 mL
2	garlic cloves, halved	2
⅓ cup	Parmesan cheese	75 mL
1 cup	fresh basil, packed	250 mL
¼-⅓ cup	olive oil	
	sea salt & pepper	

♡ Toast the pine nuts in a dry skillet or toaster oven until golden brown, stirring constantly while toasting. Let cool.

♡ In a food processor, add the peeled and halved garlic, pine nuts, Parmesan cheese, and fresh basil. Chop finely in the food processor and drizzle the olive oil through the top, until it is a beautiful smooth green thick sauce.

♡ Pour any leftover pesto into ice cube trays and freeze. Once they are frozen, remove all the pesto cubes from the ice cube tray and transfer into a freezer bag.

Yield: 10 servings or cubes
Prep Time: 20 minutes

Dressed-Up Cottage Cheese

I cannot keep this on hand for long – my kids devour it. Also great served with roast beef! Enjoy.

18 oz.	cottage cheese	500 mL
3-4	green onions, finely chopped	3-4
2-3 tsp.	chives (if in season)	10-15 mL
	sea salt & pepper	

♡ Mix all ingredients together thoroughly.

♡ Let this mixture sit for a couple of hours before you serve it – the flavors marry.

Variation:

Stuffed Red Peppers – cut 1 red pepper in half; hollow out by removing the seeds and ribs. Stuff with dressed-up cottage cheese.

Yield: 10 servings or 2½ cups (625 mL)
Serving Size: ¼ cup (60 mL)
Prep Time: 5-10 minutes

Salsa with a Twist

Who Knew?

Ketchup: Did you know that in every tablespoon (15 mL) of ketchup there is 1 tsp. (15 mL) of sugar? Yikes! A better choice would be mustard or salsa, they are much healthier and have far more flavor.

The twist here is fiber and more nutrients. I received this jazzed-up version while visiting our friends, the Brownings, in Windemere.

3 cups	store bought OR homemade salsa	750 mL
19 oz.	can chickpeas, drained	540 mL
19 oz.	can black beans, drained	540 mL
14 oz.	can niblet corn, drained	398 mL
3 tbsp.	cilantro finely chopped (optional)	45 mL

♡ Mix together all ingredients.
♡ Crack open the multigrain nacho chips and dig in.

....

For Lunches: Send a plastic container full of salsa and also a container full of multigrain chips.

Yield: 16 servings
    or 8 cups (2 L)
Serving Size: ½ cup
    (125 mL)
Prep Time: 10 minutes

Veggie Dip

½ cup	sour cream	125 mL
1 tsp.	lemon juice	5 mL
¼	red onion	¼
¼	red pepper	¼
1	garlic clove	1
1 tbsp.	mayonnaise	15 mL
½ tsp.	sea salt	2 mL
¼ tsp.	pepper	1 mL
pinch	sugar	pinch
4	fresh basil leaves or 1 tsp. (5 mL) dry basil	4

♡ In a food processor, purée all the ingredients.

♡ Let dip sit for 15 minutes and then dip away!

Yield: 1½ cups
(375 mL)
Serves: 6
Serving Size: ¼ cup
(60 mL)
Prep Time: 10 minutes

LUNCHBOX LOVE

BREADS, BISCUITS, LOAVES, & MUFFINS

Pumpkin Loaf

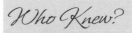

As my boyfriend Jamie Oliver says, "Easy, peasy!"

3 cups	whole-wheat flour	750 mL
1 tsp.	baking soda	5 mL
1 tsp.	sea salt	5 mL
3 tsp.	cinnamon	15 mL
1½ cups	sugar	375 mL
2 cups	canned puréed pumpkin	500 mL
4	eggs	4
1 cup	applesauce	250 mL
¼ cup	oil	60 mL

♡ In a large bowl, combine all of the dry ingredients.

♡ In a separate bowl, stir pumpkin, eggs, applesauce and oil together.

♡ Add the liquid ingredients to the dry ingredients; mix thoroughly with a wooden spoon.

♡ Pour batter into 2, 5 x 9" (13 x 23 cm) greased loaf pans.

♡ Bake at 350°F (180°C) for 1 hour.

♡ Slice loaf when cool.

....

Lunchbox Tip: Slices loaves. Place 2 slices each into individual sealable snack-size bags. Then, place the filled bags into 1 large freezer bag and label (we always think we will remember what is inside). Freeze.

To use: Place a bag of frozen slices into a lunch bag in the morning – they will be thawed in time for lunch!

Who Knew?

Spelt Flour: Spelt is a species of wheat but has less allergic qualities than regular wheat. It can be substituted whenever wheat is called for. It does however, contain gluten, so people with gluten intolerance may struggle with spelt.

Makes 2 loaves, approx. 16 slices per loaf
Yield: 32 servings
Serving Size: ½" (1 cm) slice
Prep Time: 20 minutes

Whole-Wheat Banana Bread

This recipe just begs to be doubled!

Fat: We all need fat in
our diet, children
especially need it for
brain development, the
key is the type of fat.

Previously **Coconut Oil**
had a bad wrap due to
saturated fat levels.
Studies now show the
benefits are numerous.
Due to the lauric acid
content in the fat, it is
great for the prevention
of heart disease,
increasing thyroid and
immune system
functions. Coconut oil
also provides immediate
energy and helps in
weight loss due to the
medium chain fatty acids
which are not stored as
fat, but burned for
energy and stimulates
your metabolism.

SINGLE	DOUBLE	INGREDIENTS
1 cup/250 mL	2 cups/500 mL	sugar
3	6	eggs
½ cup/125 mL	1 cup/250 mL	applesauce
¼ cup/60 mL	½ cup/125 mL	canola oil
2 cups/500 mL	4 cups/ 1 L	whole-wheat flour
2½ tsp./12 mL	5 tsp./25 mL	baking soda
½ tsp./2 mL	1 tsp./5 mL	sea salt
1 tsp./5 mL	2 tsp./10 mL	cinnamon
1 tsp./5 mL	2 tsp./10 mL	allspice
3	6	large bananas, mashed

♡ Using an electric mixer, beat sugar and eggs until creamy. Mix in applesauce and oil.

♡ In a separate bowl, whisk together flour, baking soda, sea salt, cinnamon and allspice. Add to the egg mixture. Mix in bananas; combine well.

♡ If you are making a single batch pour batter into 1 bundt pan. A double batch makes 1 bundt pan, plus 2, 4.5 x 8.5" (11.3 x 21.3 cm) loaf pans or 4 loaf pans.

♡ Bake at 350°F (180°C) for 1 hour or until done.

....

Lunchbox Tip: Cool the banana bread. Remove from the pans, set on racks. When completely cooled; slice and place 2 slices into individual sealable lunch bags. Then, place the filled bags into 1 large freezer bag and label – we always think we will remember what is inside! Freeze.

To use: Place a bag of frozen slices into a lunch bag in the morning – they will be thawed in time for lunch!

Yield: 32 servings for
single batch or
16 slices per loaf
Serving Size: ½" (1 cm)
slice
Prep Time: 20 minutes

Chocolate Chip Carrot Bread

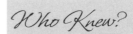

It takes a little longer to prepare this bread, due to zesting the orange and grating the carrots; but the end result is moist and fantastic! Well worth the extra few minutes.

3 cups	whole-wheat flour	750 mL
1 cup	brown sugar	250 mL
½ cup	white sugar	125 mL
4 tsp.	cinnamon	20 mL
2 tsp.	baking powder	10 mL
1 tsp.	baking soda	5 mL
1 tsp.	sea salt	5 mL
1 tsp.	ginger	5 mL
½ tsp.	cloves	2 mL
4	eggs	4
¾ cup	orange juice	175 mL
¼ cup	oil	60 mL
½ cup	applesauce	125 mL
1 tsp.	vanilla	5 mL
2 cups	grated carrots	500 mL
1 cup	chocolate chips	250 mL

♡ In a large bowl, combine all of the dry ingredients.

♡ In another bowl, beat eggs, orange juice, oil, applesauce and vanilla.

♡ Fold the wet ingredients into the dry, stirring until the mixture is moist – DO NOT OVER MIX. Fold in carrots and chocolate chips.

♡ Pour batter into 2, 5 x 9" (13 x 23 cm) greased loaf pans.

♡ Bake at 350°F (180°C) for 55-60 minutes.

....

Tip: Use a food processor to grate carrots; it is waay faster than using a grater!

Who Knew?

Dark Chocolate vs Milk Chocolate:

Dark chocolate is being praised for its flavanoids which are strong antioxidants. These antioxidants protect cells from free radical damage which can contribute to heart disease and certain types of cancers.

Yield: 32 servings
Makes: 2 loaves, approx. 16 slices per loaf
Serving Size: ½" (1 cm) slice
Prep Time: 30 minutes

Chocolate Zucchini Cake

We do whatever we can, to get more veggies in them!

4	eggs	4
2¼ cups	sugar	550 mL
2 tsp.	vanilla	10 mL
¾ cup	butter	175 mL
3 cups	whole-wheat flour	750 mL
½ cup	cocoa	125 mL
2 tsp.	baking powder	10 mL
1 tsp.	baking soda	5 mL
¾ tsp.	sea salt	3 mL
1 cup	buttermilk OR sour milk*	250 mL
3 cups	shredded zucchini	750 mL
1 cup	chocolate chips	250 mL

♡ In a large mixing bowl, beat eggs and sugar until yellow lemon colored. Add vanilla and butter, beat until smooth.

♡ In a separate bowl, combine all dry ingredients. Stir half of the dry ingredients into the egg mixture; add buttermilk or soured milk. Add the remaining flour mixture; beat until smooth.

♡ Fold in zucchini and half of the chocolate chips. Pour into a greased, 11 x 14" (28 x 36 cm) pan.

♡ Bake at 350°F (180°C) for 35 minutes or until a toothpick inserted into the center of the cake comes out clean.

♡ While cake is still warm, sprinkle the remaining chocolate chips on top. When they begin to melt, spread them evenly over the cake with a spatula.

Yield: 32 servings
Serving Size:½" (1 cm) slice
Prep Time: 20 minutes

*****To Sour Milk:** Add 1 tbsp. (15 mL) vinegar to 1 cup (250 mL) milk. Stir until milk curdles.

Apple Muffins

These are hearty and delicious and the crumbled topping adds a nice sweet crunch.

4 cups	whole-wheat flour	1 L
1 cup	sugar	250 mL
2 tbsp.	baking powder	30 mL
2 tsp.	cinnamon	10 mL
1 tsp.	sea salt	5 mL
2	unpeeled, grated apples	2
1 cup	applesauce	250 mL
2 tbsp.	canola oil	30 mL
½ cup	pecans	125 mL
3	small eggs, beaten	3
1⅓ cups	milk	325 mL

BROWN SUGAR TOPPING:

| 2 tbsp. | brown sugar | 30 mL |
| 1 tsp. | cinnamon | 5 mL |

♡ In a large bowl, combine flour, sugar, baking powder, cinnamon and sea salt.

♡ In food processor, grate apples; add to flour mixture.

♡ Stir in the remaining ingredients with a wooden spoon. DO NOT OVER MIX – the batter should be lumpy!

♡ Spoon batter into small or large muffin cups.

♡ Combine topping ingredients and sprinkle over the top of the muffins.

♡ Bake at 375° (190°C) for 20 minutes.

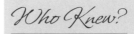
Who Knew?

Kids Cooking:
Getting kids involved in cooking teaches them reading skills, how to use an index, reading food labels, understanding weights and measurements, food and kitchen safety and how to work collaboratively with family members, which means more family time! Besides, if they prepared it, they will be more likely to eat it!

Yield = 24 muffins
Serving Size: 1 muffin
Prep Time: 20 minutes

Pumpkin Muffins

These muffins freeze well and are a fast way to load your freezer – if you can get them there!

3 cups	whole-wheat flour	750 mL
1½ cups	brown sugar (not packed)	375 mL
4 tsp.	baking powder	20 mL
1 tsp.	baking soda	5 mL
½ tsp.	allspice	2 mL
½ tsp.	nutmeg	2 mL
½ tsp.	cloves	2 mL
½ tsp.	ginger	2 mL
2 tsp.	cinnamon	10 mL
1 cup	milk	250 mL
⅔ cup	apple sauce	150 mL
1 tbsp.	canola oil	15 mL
2 cups	canned pumpkin	500 mL
2	eggs	2
1 cup	chopped dates	250 mL
1 cup	chopped pecans	250 mL

♡ Preheat oven to 375°F (190°C).

♡ In a large bowl, combine all of the dry ingredients.

♡ In a separate bowl, combine the remaining ingredients except the dates and pecans; add to the dry; DO NOT OVER MIX. Fold in dates and pecans.

♡ Bake for 20 minutes or until toothpick comes out clean.

....

Variation:

Chocolate Pumpkin Muffins: Add ¼ cup (60 mL) cocoa to ½ cup (125 mL) pumpkin muffin batter. For a marbled effect, using a knife or spatula, swirl the chocolate into the batter.

Yield: 24 muffins
Serving Size: 1 muffin
Prep Time: 20 minutes

Breads, Loaves, Muffins & Biscuits 29

Carrot Muffins

These are so moist and make a great snack with a piece of Cheddar cheese.

3 cups	whole-wheat flour	750 mL
2 tbsp.	ground flax	30 mL
4 tsp.	baking powder	20 mL
1 tsp.	sea salt	5 mL
2 tsp.	cinnamon	10 mL
½ tsp.	nutmeg	2 mL
1 cup	brown sugar	250 mL
3	eggs	3
1 cup	milk	250 mL
⅔ cup	vegetable oil	150 mL
1 tsp.	vanilla	5 mL
2 cups	grated carrots	500 mL
1 cup	raisins	250 mL

♡ Grease muffin cups or place paper-liners in muffin cups.

♡ Preheat oven to 400°F (200°C).

♡ In a large bowl, combine dry ingredients. In a separate bowl, combine the wet ingredients; then add wet to the dry ingredients, stir until well-blended. Fold in the carrots and raisins.

♡ Fill muffin cups until ⅔ full. Bake for approximately 16-20 minutes.

Yield: 24 muffins
Serving Size: 1 muffin
Prep Time: 20 minutes

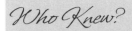

Who Knew?

Acid Reflux: Did you know kids are showing higher rates of acid reflux due to their diets? This condition is made worse from drinking pop and eating fatty foods.

Whole-Wheat Cheddar Biscuits

The nutmeg and cheese mask the whole-wheat taste – trust me! These are also great with butter and jam spread on top.

2 cups	whole-wheat flour	500 mL
4 tsp.	baking powder	20 mL
½ tsp.	sea salt	2 mL
½ tsp.	nutmeg	2 mL
4 tbsp.	softened butter	60 mL
⅔-¾ cup	milk	150-175 mL
½ cup	grated Cheddar cheese	125 mL

♡ In a bowl, whisk together flour, baking powder, salt and nutmeg. Add the butter by cutting in with a fork or pastry cutter. Mix in the Cheddar cheese. Add milk, mixing until combined.

♡ Roll out the dough to about ½" (1.3 cm) thick. Do not overwork the dough. Using a glass or biscuit cutter, cut out circles.

♡ Bake at 400°F (200°C) for 12-15 minutes. Serve warm or cold – delish!

Yield: 12 biscuits
Serving Size:1 biscuit
Prep Time: 15 minutes

Basic Dough

*This dough is used for Calzones,
Beef & Cabbage Buns and Egg Rolls.*

1½ tsp.	dry yeast	7 mL
1 cup	lukewarm water	250 mL
3 tbsp.	olive oil	45 mL
2 tsp.	honey	10 mL
1½ tsp.	sea salt	7 mL
1½ cups	white flour	375 mL
1½ cups	whole-wheat flour	375 mL

♡ In a large bowl, combine yeast, water, olive oil and honey; let sit for 5 minutes.

♡ Using a wooden spoon, mix in sea salt and flours. Once it becomes too thick and heavy to mix, turn batter out onto a floured surface. Knead until smooth.

♡ Thoroughly grease a mixing bowl with olive oil. Place dough in bowl; roll until coated in oil. Cover the bowl with a tea towel. Place in a warm spot or in an oven at the lowest temperature. Let it rise until doubled in size, about 30-60 minutes.

♡ Punch down the dough to deflate it and turn it out onto a lightly oiled surface.

♡ Bake at 350°F (180°C) for 25-30 minutes or until golden brown on bottom.

♡ See pages 40-43.

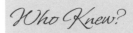

Who Knew?

Honey contains antioxidants which fight against free radical damage. It also helps in calcium absorption and has many healing properties which helps with coughs, sore throats and healing wounds. Loaded with vitamins and minerals, this is a great natural sweetener. Always buy unpasteurized honey because the heat used to pasteurize kills all the good. Also to be noted, it is the only food in your pantry that does not go bad!

Note: Do not feed unpasteurized honey to babies under 12 months old, due to the risk of botulism.

Yield: enough dough for 8 calzones, beef & cabbage buns or egg rolls
Serving Size: 8
Prep Time: 30 minutes

LUNCHBOX LOVE

SOUPS

Hamburger Borscht

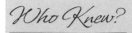
1-1½ lbs	extra-lean hamburger	500-750 g
1	onion, chopped	1
4	celery sticks, chopped	4
28 oz.	can tomatoes	796 mL
4 cups	beef broth	1 L
4	carrots	4
1	bay leaf	1
2 cups	fresh spinach OR Swiss chard OR beet tops	500 mL
5 or 6	fresh beets, pre-cooked	5 or 6
½ cup	vinegar	125 mL
1	bunch fresh baby dillweed, chopped	1
	sea salt & pepper to taste	
	sour cream for garnish	

♡ In a Dutch oven, brown the hamburger. If you are not using extra-lean beef, rinse the hamburger with boiling water once it is browned to remove excess fat.*

♡ Return beef to pot, add onions and celery; sauté until onions are transparent. Add the remaining ingredients. Simmer, covered, for 1½ hours.

♡ If you can, add the spinach and dillweed towards the end, but don't worry if you put it all in at once. Serve hot; garnish with a dollop of sour cream if desired.

....

*I am not concerned with fat, provided it is good fat. The fat in hamburger is saturated fat, which is the bad fat, this is why I want you to rinse the beef if you are not using extra-lean.

Yield: 8 servings
Serving Size: 1 cup
(250 mL)

Chicken Gumbo

This soup is absolutely fabulous.

Who Knew?

Margarine: Did you know that margarine is made by turning a liquid into a solid through a process called partial hydrogenation? The oil is extracted through high temperatures then steam cleaned (which removes the vitamins and antioxidants), but the solvents and pesticides remain. The oil is then mixed with a nickel catalyst and when it comes out it looks like gray cottage cheese and smells disgusting. Emulsifiers are added to smooth out the lumps and steam cleaned again to get rid of the disgusting smell. Then the product is bleached and a natural dye is added. Excellent ... sandwich anyone?

2 tbsp.	olive oil	30 mL
2 tbsp.	butter*	30 mL
1	medium onion, chopped	1
1	red pepper, chopped	1
2	celery stalks	2
2	garlic cloves	2
3	skinless boneless chicken breasts, cubed	3
3 tbsp.	flour	45 mL
2 x 10 oz.	cans chicken broth	2 x 398 mL
7½ oz.	can diced tomatoes	213 mL
1 tsp.	sea salt	5 mL
½ tsp.	pepper	2 mL
½ tsp.	tabasco or to taste	2 mL

♡ In a large pot, melt butter and olive oil. Add onion, red pepper, celery and garlic; sauté for 5-6 minutes.

♡ Add chicken and sauté until chicken is cooked through. Stir in flour, continue cooking, stirring often, until the chicken starts to brown. Stir in broth, tomatoes, sea salt and pepper. Mix in hot sauce. Cook on medium heat until gumbo is bubbly and hot.

....

* You can use 4 tbsp. (90 mL) of butter and omit the olive oil, but I use half olive oil and half butter because olive oil is a better fat.

Yield: 6 servings
Serving Size: 1 cup
(250 mL)
Prep Time: 20 minutes

Spicy Tomato Soup

This is fast and easy!

1 cup	whole-wheat elbow pasta	250 mL
½	red onion, chopped	½
2	garlic cloves	2
1	red or green pepper	1
12 oz.	can tomato juice OR V8	355 mL
14 oz.	can corn or 1 cup (250 mL) frozen corn	398 mL
14 oz.	can black beans	398 mL
¼ cup	salsa	60 mL
1 tsp.	oregano	5 mL
1 tsp.	basil	5 mL
¼-½ tsp.	red pepper flakes (optional)	1-2 mL
	grated Cheddar cheese	
	sour cream	

♡ Cook pasta until al dente (meaning it is still slightly firm), drain and rinse.

♡ In a large saucepan, sauté onion, garlic and pepper until soft. Add the remaining ingredients and simmer for 30 minutes. Garnish with Cheddar and sour cream.

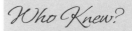
Beans are an excellent source of protein and fibre. After a meal, they are a great blood sugar leveler and help to lower cholesterol. Beans contain a molybdenum which helps to detoxify sulphites, which are preservatives in prepared foods. It is amazing that beans also contain 10 times more antioxidants than an orange.

Yield: 6 servings
Serving Size: 1 cup
(250 mL)
Prep Time: 20 minutes

Carrot and Sweet Potato Soup

This soup is low-fat, fabulous and creamy.
It tastes decadent – but isn't.

1 tbsp.	olive oil	15 mL
2	garlic cloves, crushed	2
1	large onion, chopped	1
4 cups	chicken stock	1 L
1	small potato, peeled and chopped	1
6	carrots, peeled and chopped	6
1	large sweet potato, peeled and chopped	1
2 tbsp.	chopped, fresh tarragon OR 1 tsp. (5 mL) dried	30 mL
	sea salt & pepper, to taste	

♡ In a large skillet, over medium heat, sauté onion and garlic in oil until soft. Add all the other ingredients except for fresh herbs. Simmer on low for 45 minutes.

♡ With a hand blender, purée mixture until creamy and smooth. Stir in tarragon or dillweed, sea salt and pepper.

....

Tip: If you don't have a hand blender, use an electric blender. Process in batches.

Yield: 6 servings
Serving Size: 1 cup
　　　　　(250 mL)
Prep Time: 30 minutes

Soups 37

Cream Cheese Chicken Soup

This is a super silky, smooth soup!

1	onion, chopped	1
2	garlic cloves	2
1 tbsp.	olive oil	15 mL
4 cups	chicken broth	1 L
3	carrots	3
1	large sweet potato, peeled and chopped	
2	skinless, boneless chicken breasts, cubed	2
	sea salt & pepper	
¼ cup	flour	60 mL
1 cup	milk	250 mL
8 oz.	pkg. cream cheese, cubed	250 g
2 tbsp.	fresh parsley	30 mL

♡ In a saucepan, sauté onion and garlic in olive oil. Add the broth, carrots, sweet potatoes and chicken. Bring to a boil, reduce heat, cover and simmer until vegetables are tender and the chicken is cooked through. Add sea salt and pepper to taste.

♡ In a small cup, combine flour and milk until smooth. Stir the flour mixture into the soup. Bring to a boil; cook and stir until thickened. Reduce heat, stir in the cream cheese until melted. Stir in the parsley.

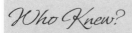

Who Knew?

Microwaving: There are several studies out, that show that microwaving food destroys the vital nutrients needed by the body. We are essentially eating "dead food", there is no nutritional value. To be on the safe side, I send heated soup in a thermos container to school. This eliminates the line-ups for the microwave to heat up their food in a plastic container, that will just leach chemicals into it anyway!

Yield: 6 servings
Serving Size: 1 cup
(250 mL)
Prep Time: 20 minutes

LUNCHBOX LOVE

SANDWICHES,
WRAPS
&
PIZZAS

Calzones

I typically make the filling the day before I make Calzones, Cabbage and Beef Buns, Samosas or Egg Roll Buns.

1 tbsp.	olive oil	15 mL
2	garlic cloves, minced	2
1	medium onion, chopped	1
¼ cup	chopped mushrooms	60 mL
1	green pepper, chopped	1
1	eggplant, diced	1
6 oz.	pkg. fresh cherry or grape tomatoes	170 g
2 cups	tomato sauce	500 mL
2 tsp.	dried basil	10 mL
½ tsp.	honey	2 mL
½ cup	Parmesan cheese	
	sea salt & pepper to taste	
	basic dough, see page 32	

♡ In a large skillet, sauté the onion, garlic, and mushrooms until soft. Add the peppers, eggplant and grape tomatoes; cook until softened. Add the tomato sauce, honey, basil, salt and pepper. Simmer for 10-15 minutes then stir in the Parmesan, until melted. Allow the filling to cool before putting into dough.

♡ Divide the dough into 8 pieces. Roll each piece to approximately ⅛" (3 mm) thickness. Cut into a 6" (15 cm) round circle. Place the filling on one side and fold the other half over to make a half moon. Press edges together ensuring they are well sealed by pressing down with a fork.

Who Knew?

Tomatoes & Lycopene: Tomatoes, are not only a great source of Vitamin A, Vitamin C and Vitamin K, they contain a carotenoid that is called Lycopene. Lycopene is an amazing antioxidant that has been shown to help prevent heart disease and many cancers including colorectal, prostate, breast, endometrial, lung and pancreatic. Lycopene is the ingredient in tomatoes that makes them red. Canned and cooked tomatoes also contain lycopene.

♡ MAKE SURE THE BUNS ARE COMPLETELY SEALED, SO THE FILLING WON'T LEAK OUT.

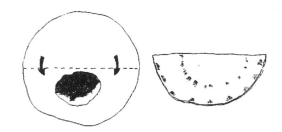

♡ Bake at 350°F (180°C) for 25-30 minutes until the bottoms are golden.

Yield: 8 calzones
Serving Size: 1 calzone
Prep Time: 30 minutes for filling; 30 minutes for dough – but don't forget about the rising time.

Beef and Cabbage Buns

Don't be shy to pack in the meat for another amazing lunch time sandwich alternative.

1 lb.	lean ground beef	500 g
1	medium onion, chopped	1
2	garlic cloves, minced	2
1 cup	finely chopped mushrooms	250 mL
4	celery stalks, chopped	4
¼	head small cabbage, finely chopped	¼
2 tsp.	dried basil	10 mL
	sea salt & pepper to taste	
	basic dough, see page 32	

♥ In a large skillet, brown the ground beef, onion and garlic together until cooked.

♥ Add the remaining ingredients and simmer until the cabbage has softened. Allow the filling to cool.

♥ Divide the dough into 8 pieces. Take each piece and roll it out very thinly, approximately ⅛" (3 mm) thick. The squares should be about 6" (15 cm). Don't worry about making the squares perfect – it really doesn't matter!

♥ Place 1 filling portion into middle of 1 dough square. Fold the corners of the dough towards the middle, pinch the flaps together, forming a sealed bun. Flip the bun over so that the seams are on the bottom and use your hands to shape each bun. MAKE SURE THE BUNS ARE COMPLETELY SEALED, SO THE FILLING WON'T LEAK OUT.

♥ Bake at 350°F (180°C) for 25-30 minutes until the bottoms are golden.

Who Knew?

Cabbage is a great source of vitamin C, fibre and nutrition. It also helps to burn fat.

Who Knew?

Sesame seeds are rich in beneficial minerals and dietary fiber. They have been shown to have cholesterol lowering effects in humans thanks to their beneficial fibers called "lignans".

2	large chicken breasts,	2
½	medium onion, chopped	½
2-4	garlic cloves, minced	2-4
½ cup	chopped mushrooms	125 mL
2	carrots, chopped	2
¼	head, small cabbage, chopped	¼
1 tsp.	ginger root	5 mL
2 tbsp.	toasted sesame seeds	30 mL
½ cup	tamari OR light soy sauce	125 mL
1 tsp.	sesame oil	5 mL
	sea salt & pepper to taste	
	basic dough, see page 32	

♡ In a large skillet, sauté the chicken breasts until thoroughly cooked. Remove from heat; cut into small pieces.

♡ In a food processor, pulse the onion, garlic, mushrooms, carrots and cabbage, 2 or 3 times, so it is a bit chunky.

♡ In a clean skillet over medium heat, add chicken and onion mixture. Stir in ginger, sesame seeds and tamari sauce; cook for approximately 5 minutes. Add the sesame oil, season with salt and pepper. Cool.

♡ Divide the dough into 8 pieces. Roll out very thinly, about ⅛" (3 mm) thick. The squares should be 6" (15 cm) but don't worry about making the squares perfect!

♡ Place the filling in the middle of each square. Fold the corners of the dough towards the middle, pinch the flaps together, forming a sealed bun. Flip the bun over so that the seams are on the bottom and use your hands to shape each bun. MAKE SURE THE BUNS ARE COMPLETELY SEALED, SO THE FILLING WON'T LEAK OUT.

♡ Bake at 350°F (180°C) for 25-30 minutes until the bottoms are golden.

Yield: 8 buns
Serving Size: 1 square bun
Prep Time: 30 minutes for filling; 30 minutes for dough – but don't forget about the dough rising time.

Samosa Buns

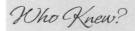

These are a milder version of samosas, but still very flavorful.

1	large chicken breast, approximately ½ lb. (250 g)	1
1 tsp.	olive oil	5 mL
2 tsp.	butter	10 mL
½	large onion, chopped	½
2	garlic cloves, minced	
1 tbsp.	flour	
1 tsp.	curry powder*	
½ cup	chicken OR vegetable stock	125 mL
½ cup	frozen peas	125 mL
½ cup	frozen or canned corn	125 mL
	sea salt & pepper to taste	

SAMOSA DOUGH:

1½ cups	white, unbleached flour	375 mL
1 cup	whole-wheat flour	250 mL
1 cup	yogurt	250 mL
½ tsp.	sea salt	2 mL
2 tbsp.	olive oil	30 mL

♡ In a large skillet, sauté the chicken in the olive oil and butter. Once the chicken is almost cooked through, add the onion and garlic; continue cooking until they are soft and transparent. Add the flour and curry powder; sauté for 1 minute, stirring constantly. Add the chicken stock and stir until the sauce begins to thicken slightly. Add the peas and corn and cook until warmed through. Season with sea salt and pepper. Allow the filling to cool before putting into dough.

Who Knew?

Turmeric is the yellow in curry powder and is a natural antibiotic. It promotes proper metabolism and aids in digestion. Not to mention it tastes great!

Samosa Buns

continued

♡ In a bowl, mix the flour and sea salt together. Make a well in the middle. Pour the yogurt and canola oil into the middle. Gradually stir the flour into the liquid until it forms a ball. Knead lightly and let sit.

♡ Divide the filling and dough into 12 even portions. Roll each piece of dough into a thin circle, approximately ⅛" (3 mm) thick. (This dough is a "tougher" dough than the basic dough – it is also firmer and thicker and is harder to roll out.) Place the filling on one side of the circle, fold the dough over the filling and pinch together the sides. Make sure the samosa is well sealed by pressing the edges together with a fork.

♡ Bake at 400°F (200°C) for 15 minutes. Reduce heat to 350°F (180°C) and bake for another 10 minutes.

....

Tip: If your children are new to curry, start with ½ tsp. (2 mL) – add more or not, if desired.

Yield: 12 buns
Serving Size: 1 bun
Prep Time: 30 minutes for filling; 30 minutes for dough

...ish Pasties

*jazzed-up version of Cornish Pasties. I
...eed since this is an English dish and bland is
t.. ...ame of the game. Sorry Mum, and all you Brits,
but you know who you are!*

FILLING:

1 lb.	lean ground beef	500 g
1	medium onion, finely chopped	1
2	garlic cloves	2
1	carrot, finely diced	1
2	celery stalks, finely diced	2
½ cup	mushrooms, finely chopped	125 mL
¼ cup	frozen peas	60 mL
¼ cup	sour cream	60 mL
	sea salt & pepper to taste	

DOUGH:

3 cups	whole-wheat flour	750 mL
¾ tsp.	sea salt	175 mL
2 tbsp.	baking powder	30 mL
6 tbsp.	butter	90 mL
¾ cup	grated Cheddar cheese	175 mL
1¼ cups	cooked and mashed sweet potato	300 mL

♡ FILLING: In a food processor, pulse the onions, garlic, carrots, celery and mushrooms, 2 or 3 times. Don't purée the filling, it should have a slightly chunky texture. This is extremely helpful if a child does not like a particular ingredient – they tend not to notice, if it is finely chopped.

Cornish Pasties

continued

♡ Sauté the ground beef until thoroughly cooked. Add the vegetable mixture; cook for 5 minutes. Then add the peas and heat through, stir in the sour cream, sea salt and pepper. Remove from heat and let the mixture cool, while you prepare the dough.

♡ DOUGH: In a food processor, place the flour, sea salt, baking powder, butter, cheese and sweet potato; pulse until all combined. Slowly add the milk while the processor is still running, until the dough forms a ball.

♡ Place the dough out onto a floured surface. Knead until the dough forms a ball. The dough should not be sticky, so add more flour as necessary.

♡ Divide your filling and dough into 12 even portions. Roll each piece of dough into a thin circle, approximately ⅛" (3 mm) thick. Place the filling on one side of the circle, fold the dough over the filling and pinch the sides together. Make sure the dough is well-sealed, by pressing the edges together with a fork.

♡ Bake at 400°F (200°C) for 15-18 minutes.

Yield: 12 pasties
Serving Size: 1 pastie
Prep Time: 1 hour for filling , dough and assembly

Quiche Cups

These use a lot of eggs but are worth it. They are a cross between a quiche and a muffin all-in-one, and they're easy to pack. My kids go crazy for them and will eat 2 for lunch. Great served with salsa!

6	eggs	6
½ cup	vegetable oil	125 mL
1¼ cups	whole-wheat flour	300 mL
1 tbsp.	baking powder	15 mL
1 tsp.	dried basil	5 mL
1	garlic clove	1
	sea salt & pepper	
1½ cups	finely chopped broccoli	375 mL
½	red pepper, finely chopped	½
1 cup	cooked chicken OR turkey OR ham	250 mL
1	medium onion	1
1 cup	grated Cheddar cheese	250 mL

♡ In a large bowl, beat the eggs until they are very foamy. Add the vegetable oil and mix well.

♡ In a small bowl, combine the flour, baking powder, basil, garlic, salt and pepper; mix into the egg mixture. Stir in the broccoli, red pepper, meat, onion and cheese.

♡ Spoon into greased muffin cups.

♡ Bake at 375°F (190°C) for 20-25 minutes.

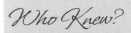

Who Knew?

Eggs promote healthy hair and nails due to their high sulphur content. They are also one of the only foods that naturally contain vitamin D.

Yield: 12 large muffins
Serving Size: 1 muffin
Prep Time: 20 minutes

Freezer Burritos

My kids love these cold, but they are great warmed up as well.

3 lbs.	extra-lean ground beef	1.5 kg
4 oz.	can jalapenos, chopped	114 mL
2 cups	salsa	500 mL
14 oz.	can black olives, (optional)	398 mL
1	bunch green onions	1
24	whole-wheat tortilla shells	24
14 oz.	can refried beans	39 mL
	Cheddar cheese, grated	

♡ In a large skillet, brown and drain ground beef.

♡ In a large bowl, combine beef, jalapenos, salsa, black olives and green onions.

♡ Place a tortilla shell on a flat surface. Spread a small amount of beans on the shell, add the ground beef mixture, sprinkle with cheese. Roll up the shell, tucking in both ends as you go.

♡ Individually wrap each burrito in plastic wrap and put them in freezer bags; freeze. To use, remove burrito from the freezer the night before, refrigerate and it will be thawed by morning.

....

Quick Supper Idea: Take out 1 burrito for each member of your family. Place in a casserole; cover with grated cheese and bake at 350°F (180°C) for about 20 minutes, or until heated through. Garnish with green onions, sour cream and more salsa if desired. Serve with a fresh salad.

Who Knew?

Salsa is an excellent alternative to ketchup. It adds tons of flavor but does not contain the sugar of ketchup.

Yield: 24 burritos
Serving Size: 1 burrito
Prep Time: 1 hour

Quesadillas

This is one of my kids' favorites! I make them the night before, so they are completely cooled. Cut into 6 wedges and include small containers of sour cream, salsa and guacamole for dipping.

2	100% whole-wheat tortilla wraps	2
½	cooked chicken breast, finely chopped	½
2 tbsp.	red OR green pepper, finely chopped	30 mL
2 tbsp.	finely chopped red onion	30 mL
¼ tsp.	dried basil	1 mL
2 tbsp.	grated Cheddar OR mozzarella cheese	30 mL

OTHER ADDITIONS:
black beans
sweet potatoes
sliced tomato
cheeses, different types of
cooked hamburger
fresh cilantro

♡ In a skillet on medium heat, place 1 wrap on bottom. Spread the chicken, pepper, onion and basil evenly over the wrap. Sprinkle with grated cheese. Place the second tortilla on top.

♡ Cook until the bottom wrap gets a bit brown. To flip; place a spatula underneath and lift the quesadilla up. Pull the frying pan out from underneath and turn it upside down and place on top of the quesadilla. Turn over so that the uncooked wrap is on the bottom of the pan. Cook until the wrap is browned and the cheese is melted.

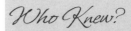

Who Knew?

Basil has shown to inhibit the growth of bacteria and also has anti-inflammatory qualities. Not to mention it is a good source of vitamin A, which prevents damage to cells by free radicals.

Experiment and use whatever ingredients your kids like!

Yield: 1 quesadilla
Prep Time: 15 minutes

Tortilla Pizzas

You can be creative with the toppings, choose what your kids like and make them a fun and nutritious snack or lunch.

whole-wheat tortilla wraps
tomato sauce
Italian seasoning

HAWAIIAN PIZZA TOPPING:
ham
pineapple
tomato sauce
mozzarella cheese

CHICKEN PIZZA TOPPING:
cooked chicken
red pepper
red onion
basil
tomato sauce
mozzarella cheese

MARGHERITA PIZZA TOPPING:
fresh tomato, sliced
fresh basil
mozzarella cheese

♡ Place a whole-wheat wrap on a baking sheet. Spread a thin layer of tomato sauce and Italian seasoning (or basil, oregano, salt and pepper) over top.

♡ Cover with any of the suggested toppings.

♡ Bake at 350°F (180°C) for about 5 minutes or until the cheese melts.

Pita or Wrap Fillings

Here are some easy fillings that are absolutely delicious. You can change or delete any of the ingredients to meet your child's' preferences. Experiment a little; they might surprise you!

TUNA WRAP:

⅓	6.5 oz. (184 g) can tuna	⅓
1	boiled egg, chopped finely	1
3 or 4	fresh green beans	3 or 4
2 or 3	cherry tomatoes, halved	2 or 3
1	green onion, chopped	1
1 tbsp.	mayonnaise	15 mL
1 or 2	lettuce leaves	1 or 2

NUTTY CHICKEN:

1 cup	leftover cooked chicken OR turkey	250 mL
2-3 tbsp.	grated cheese	30-45 mL
2 tsp.	cashews, almonds, OR pumpkin seeds, minced and toasted	10 mL
½	celery stalk, finely chopped	½
¼	red pepper, finely chopped	¼
1	green onion, chopped	1
1 tbsp.	mayonnaise	15 mL
1 or 2	lettuce leaves	1 or 2

CHICKEN CURRY :

1 cup	leftover cooked chicken OR turkey	250 mL
5 or 6	grapes, chopped	5 or 6
2-3 tbsp.	grated cheese	30-45 mL
½	celery stalk, finely chopped	½
1 tbsp.	mayonnaise	15 mL
½ tsp.	curry powder (mix with mayonnaise)	2 mL
1 or 2	lettuce leaves	1 or 2

Who Knew?

Nuts: By throwing in a handful of nuts (your choice) to a wrap or pita filling, they will add good fat and protein and also add a great crunch.

HAM, CHICKEN, HAM & CHEESE:

1 cup	cooked chicken OR turkey	250 mL
1	slice ham	1
2-3 tbsp.	grated cheese	30-45 mL
1	boiled egg, chopped finely	1
½	celery stalk, chopped	½
1 tbsp.	mayonnaise	15 mL
1 or 2	lettuce leaves	1 or 2

PESTO, TOMATO CHICKEN:

1 cup	cooked chicken OR turkey	250 mL
3-4	cherry tomatoes, quartered	3-4
1-2 tsp.	pesto sauce	5-10 mL
1 or 2	lettuce leaves	1 or 2

RED PEPPER HUMMUS:

¼	red pepper, cut in strips	¼
1	carrot, grated	1
2 or 3	cherry tomatoes, halved	2 or 3
3 or 4	snow peas	3 or 4
1-2 tbsp.	hummus	15-30 mL
1 or 2	lettuce leaves	1 or 2

ALMOND CRANBERRY CHICKEN:

1 cup	cooked, finely chopped chicken OR turkey	250 mL
3	green onions, chopped	3
¼ cup	toasted, chopped almonds	60 mL
2 tbsp.	dried cranberries	30 mL
1	celery stalk, chopped	1
1 tbsp.	mayonnaise	15 mL
1 tsp.	lemon juice	5 mL

♡ Combine ingredients for any of the suggested fillings.

♡ Spread filling onto a wrap or fill a pita.

Green Egg Salad

Don't be turned off by the name – this is fabulous and again the avocado adds good fat to the sandwich.

3	eggs, hard-boiled and mashed	3
2	green onions, chopped	2
3 or 4	chives, chopped (optional)	3 or 4
1	celery stalk, finely chopped	1
2 tsp.	mayonnaise	10 mL
¼	red pepper, finely chopped	¼
½	avocado, mashed	½
1 tsp.	lemon juice	5 mL
	sea salt & pepper	
2	large dill pickles, finely chopped	2

♡ Combine all the ingredients.

♡ Use as a sandwich filling on a sandwich, topped with a lettuce leaf.

Variation:

Tuna Salad: Substitute a 6.5 oz. (184 g) can of tuna instead of the egg. Add finely chopped red or green pepper.

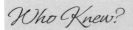
Yield: 4 servings
Serving Size: ½ cup (125 mL)
Prep Time: 10 minutes once eggs are cooked

Egg Wraps

I slice these into little pinwheels, or you can leave them whole and serve as a wrap.

5	eggs	5
2 tbsp.	yogurt	30 mL
3	green onions, chopped	3
½ tsp.	dried basil	2 mL

EGG WRAP FILLERS:
  turkey, chicken or tuna
  red pepper strips
  cheese slices (not processed
    cheese slices)
  green pepper strips
  lettuce
  green beans

♥ Whisk all of the ingredients together.

♥ In a non-stick pan over a medium-high heat, pour in enough of the egg mixture to cover the bottom of the pan with a thin layer. Cook until the top is fully set.

♥ Roll up the egg wrap using any of the fillers; or use whatever fillers your children prefer.

♥ Slice into pinwheels or serve as a wrap.

Eggs: Did you know that by the time eggs get to the grocery store, they can be 4-weeks old? For the freshest and best eggs, talk to a local farmer or go to your nearest Farmers' Market. Their eggs are usually only a day- or two-old when you buy them. Not to mention the chickens have had a much better life, so you can feel good about eating them!

Yield: 5 servings
Prep Time: 30 minutes

Lunch-on-a-Stick

You can make this for supper and have enough left-overs for lunches the next day. They are great served with a little Tzaziki for dipping.

CHICKEN LUNCH-ON-A-STICK:

> skinless, boneless chicken
> breasts, 1 per person
> add extra for lunches

LEMON GARLIC MARINADE:

½ cup	olive oil	125 mL
¼ cup	lemon juice	60 mL
1	garlic clove, crushed	1
½ tsp.	oregano	2 mL
	sea salt & pepper	

♡ Cut raw chicken into chunks about 1½" (4 cm) square.

♡ Combine the marinade ingredients and pour over the chicken. Marinate the chicken for at least an hour or overnight – the longer the better.

♡ Soak bamboo skewers in cold water for 30 minutes. Thread the chicken on the skewers.

♡ Grill on barbecue or in the oven approximately 15 minutes or until the chicken is thoroughly cooked.

♡ Serve with raw vegetables and tzaziki. Wrap in a pita or send separately.

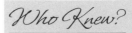

Who Knew?

Hot dogs are the bain of my existence. It seems that just about every school has a hot dog program. My kids old school had it every Thursday and it made me crazy. The problem I have with hot dogs are that they are made with by-product meats e.g.; as my Dad who was a butcher used to say, lips and ***holes.

They also contain many harmful and cancer causing chemicals that are used to improve appearance and taste.

Yield: 8 servings
Serving Size: 1 stick
Prep Time: 20 minutes

Who Knew?

continued:

Hot dogs: Some of these chemicals are sodium nitrite which is a color keeper and sodium nitrate which is a preservative. For more scary information that should make you run screaming from the hot dog and processed meat isle, check out the websites listed on page 77.

BEEF LUNCH-ON-A-STICK:

2 lbs.	extra-lean ground beef	1 kg
1	egg	1
1 tbsp.	basil	15 mL
1 tbsp.	oregano	15 mL
1 tsp.	garlic powder	5 mL
1 tsp.	onion powder	5 mL
1 tsp.	sea salt	5 mL
½ tsp.	pepper	2 mL

♡ Mix together all of the ingredients. Form into 1½" (4 cm) wide x 6" (15 cm) long logs. Push the skewer through the middle of the beef log and broil at 375°F (190°C) for 30-45 minutes.

♡ Remove the chicken or beef from the skewers when packing in lunches so that the kids are not taking the skewers to school. Place the chicken or beef stick on a pita. Spread with hummus or Tzaziki, a little bit of crumbled feta cheese and shredded lettuce. Wrap up.

Yield: 12 servings
Serving Size: 1 stick
Prep Time: 20

Chicken Drumsticks

Place leftovers of this supper dish, in sealed containers and refrigerate. Add to lunches in the morning, remember to send a freezer pack along with the lunch to keep the chicken cold. You need to make lots if you want leftovers, as they seem to disappear fast!

12	chicken drumsticks, skin removed	12

HONEY, GARLIC SAUCE:

⅓ cup	honey	75 mL
2-3	garlic cloves, crushed	2-3
3 tbsp.	soy sauce	45 mL
1 tbsp.	sesame oil	15 mL
½ tsp.	red pepper flakes	2 mL
2 tsp.	fresh grated ginger	10 mL
3 tbsp.	water	45 mL
1 tbsp.	olive oil	15 mL

♡ In a saucepan of hot water, boil the drumsticks for 20 minutes or until mostly cooked. If the chicken is frozen you can boil it without defrosting; it will just take a little longer to cook through.

♡ While the chicken is boiling, combine the sauce ingredients.

♡ Drain the chicken. When it is cool enough to handle, remove the skin. This is really easy to do once the chicken has been boiled.

♡ If you have time marinate the drumsticks for 1 hour or longer in the prepared sauce. If you don't have the time to marinate, just place the drumsticks in a flat baking dish and pour the sauce over top.

♡ Bake at 375°F (190°C) for 20-30 minutes, basting and turning frequently.

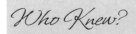

Who Knew?

Chickens: Did you know that chickens are the most abused animal on the planet? They are packed by the thousands into sheds and fed huge amounts of antibiotics and drugs to keep them alive, in conditions that would otherwise kill them. Seven weeks after they are born, they are transported to slaughterhouses, often through all weather extremes, without any food or water. They are often scalded to death and have their sensitive beaks cut off with a hot blade. The "Humane Slaughter Act" exempts birds. *Go figure!*

Yield: 12 servings
Serving Size: 1 drumstick
Prep Time: 20 minutes

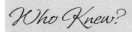
Chicken Fingers

These are healthier than the deep-fried version. The oatmeal and flax add fiber and flax is very heart-healthy. My kids love these served cold with plum sauce or ketchup for dipping.

| 6 | chicken breasts, cut into strips | 6 |
| 2 cups | plain yogurt | 500 L |

BREADING:

2 cups	oatmeal	500 mL
½ cup	ground flax	125 mL
1 tsp.	garlic powder	5 mL
1 tsp.	onion powder	5 mL
	sea salt & pepper	

♡ Place chicken strips in a bowl and cover with yogurt. Marinate from 30 minutes up to 2 hours.

♡ In a food processor, coarsely grind the oatmeal.

♡ Mix the ground flax, garlic, onion powder, salt and pepper with the oatmeal.

♡ Dip chicken into the oatmeal mixture.

♡ Place on an oiled cookie sheet and bake at 350°F (180°C) for 15 minutes until golden brown.

Yield: 24 chicken fingers
Serving Size: 1 chicken finger
Prep Time: 20 minutes

Featherless Chicken Nuggets

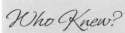

I make a bunch of these ahead of time and freeze them, then thaw what I need. This recipe is for 2 chicken breasts so, double or triple the recipe as needed. Dip in hoisin sauce … so good!

2	chicken breasts, boneless, skinless, and cut into chunks	2
2	celery stalks	2
4	strips red, green, or orange pepper	4
1	egg	
¼ cup	bread crumbs	60 mL
1 tbsp.	grated ginger	15 mL
2	garlic loves, minced	2
1 tbsp.	sesame oil	15 mL
	sea salt & pepper	

♥ In a food processor, coarsely chop all the ingredients . Do not purée!

♥ Roll mixture into balls place on an oiled cookie sheet, squash down with a fork.

♥ Bake at 350°F (180°C) for 15-18 minutes or until golden brown. These are great for dipping or eating plain.

♥ **To make nuggets**: Use the breading recipe on page 45. Dip in egg and roll in the breading. Bake as above.

....

Yield: 12 servings
Serving Size: 1 nugget

Who Knew?

Do you know what is in that **Chicken Nugget** that you are ordering for your kids? Let me give you a few examples of their 38 ingredients. Corn – of every description … fillers mainly! The hydrogenated oil can come from soybeans, canola, or cotton (yes, you read right, cotton) and several synthetic ingredients that are byproducts of a petroleum refinery or chemical plant. A whole long list of chemicals that are carcinogens and reproductive effectors. Oh, and it is also flammable. And the best part – something called tertiary butylhydroquinone (TBHQ) which is made from petroleum and is sprayed either on the nugget or inside the box to "help preserve freshness". This is a form of butane – you know lighter fluid? Thankfully the FDA has only allowed processors to use this "sparingly", I say thankfully because eating a single gram of TBHQ can cause "nausea, vomiting, ringing in the ears, delirium, a sense of suffocation, and collapse." Eating five grams of TBHQ can – wait for it – kill you! Chicken nugget anyone?

The Omnivore's Dilemma by Michael Pollan

LUNCHBOX LOVE

DESSERTS & SNACKS

Chocolate Surprise Cookies

The less your children know about what is in these cookies – the better. Just watch them disappear.

½ cup	butter	125 mL
1 cup	brown sugar	250 mL
1 tsp.	vanilla	5 mL
2	eggs	2
19 oz.	can chickpeas, drained and rinsed OR any type of white bean	540 mL
2 cups	ground, rolled oats*	500 mL
1 cup	whole-wheat flour	250 mL
2 tbsp.	ground flax meal	30 mL
½ cup	cocoa	125 mL
1 tsp.	baking soda	5 mL
1 tsp.	baking powder	5 mL
½ tsp.	sea salt	2 mL
1 cup	chocolate OR white chocolate chips	250 mL
½ cup	pecans	125 mL

♡ With an electric mixer, in a large bowl, cream together butter and sugar.

♡ In a food processor, purée the chickpeas until smooth. For a smoother consistency, add 1 tbsp. (15 mL) water.

♡ To the butter mixture, mix in the vanilla, eggs and chickpeas.

♡ In another bowl, combine the oats, flour, cocoa, flax meal, baking soda, baking powder and salt. Stir the dry ingredients into the wet. Fold in the chocolate chips and pecans.

♡ Drop by spoonfuls onto greased cookie sheets. Dip a fork into water; press down into each cookie. Since these are denser they will not flatten from baking, they will stay as balls.

♡ Bake at 350°F (180°C) for 14-16 minutes.

Who Knew?

Cacao nibs are the raw form of cocoa known as cacao beans. They are rich in magnesium, sulfur, (detoxifies the liver and supports healthy pancreas function). They also contain 10 g of antioxidants for every 100 g of beans.

Variation:

Triple Chocolate Cookies, add ¼ cup (60 mL) raw cacao nibs.

....

*Use a food processor to grind the rolled oats, being careful to not grind it into flour.

....

Yield: 48 cookies

Prep Time: 20 minutes

Ginger Chocolate Chip Cookies

Our family loves ginger cookies. So, this is my healthier verison. These are not like a gingersnaps they have a softer consistency.

½ cup	butter	125 mL
1 cup	sugar	250 mL
14 oz.	can white, cannellini or navy beans OR chick peas	398 mL
1	egg	1
¼ cup	molasses	60 mL
2¾ cups	whole-wheat flour	675 mL
1 tsp.	EACH cloves, ginger and cinnamon	5 mL
2 tsp.	baking soda	10 mL
¼ tsp.	salt	2 mL
1 cup	chocolate chips	250 mL
½ cup	chopped pecan (optional)	125 mL
¼ cup	cacao nibs (optional)	60 mL

♡ Cream butter and sugar together.

♡ Rinse and drain beans or chickpeas. Process in a food processor until completely puréed (add 1 tbsp./15 mL of water if necessary).

♡ Stir the beans into the butter and sugar mixture; add the egg and molasses, until completely incorporated.

♡ In a separate bowl, mix together all the dry ingredients. Gradually add to the wet. Mix until well blended.

♡ Fold in the chocolate chips and pecans. With a spatula dipped in water, flatten the cookies, as they will not spread while baking.

♡ Bake at 350°F (180°C) for 10-12 minutes.

Yield: 48 cookies
Prep Time: 20 minutes

Kitchen Sink Cookies

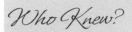

These have everything but the kitchen sink in them!

¾ cup	butter	175 mL
¼ cup	applesauce	60 mL
1 tsp.	vanilla	5 mL
3	eggs	3
1 cup	brown sugar	250 mL
2 cups	whole-wheat flour	500 mL
1½ tsp.	baking powder	7 mL
1½ tsp.	baking soda	7 mL
1 cup	coconut	250 mL
1 cup	oatmeal	250 mL
1 cup	puffed rice	250 mL
1 cup	raisins	250 mL
1 cup	chocolate chips	250 mL
¾ cup	sunflower seeds	175 mL
½ cup	sesame seeds	125 mL
⅓ cup	ground flax	75 mL
⅓ cup	wheat germ	75 mL

♡ In a large bowl, beat together butter, applesauce, sugar, vanilla and eggs. Mix in flour, baking soda and baking powder, until well blended. Stir in remaining ingredients.

♡ Roll dough into balls and flatten with a fork. I use a medium size ice cream scoop to prevent my hands from getting mucky!

♡ Bake at 350°F (180°C) for 10 minutes.

....

Note: I add flax into all of my recipes, but remember if you add in a certain amount of flax you must remove the same amount of flour or the batter/dough will be very dry.

Who Knew?

Flax is an excellent source of omega-3 fatty acids. It reduces high-blood pressure and boosts the immune system. It is also loaded with fibre and has many other benefits. To maintain freshness, it is best to store flax seed in the freezer.

Yield: 48 servings
Prep Time: 20 minutes

Mini-Power Bites

I had a cookie similar to this in an organic grocery store. I took one home and this is my version!

2 cups	rolled oats	500 mL
1 cup	whole-wheat flour	250 mL
¼ cup	cocoa	60 mL
¾ cup	sugar	60 mL
1 tsp.	cinnamon	5 mL
½ tsp.	sea salt	2 mL
¼ cup	flax	60 mL
1 cup	chocolate chips	250 mL
1 cup	raisins	250 mL
½ cup	sunflower seeds	125 mL
1 cup	pumpkin seeds	250 mL
½ cup	coconut	125 mL
½ cup	milk (dairy, almond OR rice)	125 mL
½ cup	canola oil	125 mL
1 tbsp.	molasses* OR 2 tbsp. (30 mL) honey	15 mL
1	egg	1

♡ In a large mixing bowl, combine the oats, flour, cocoa, sugar, cinnamon, sea salt, flax, chocolate chips, raisins, sunflower seeds, pumpkin seeds and coconut.

♡ Stir in the milk, oil, molasses or honey and egg; mix well with a wooden spoon.

♡ Spoon the mix onto a greased cookie sheet with a teaspoon

♡ Bake at 350°F (180°C) for 10 minutes.

....

*Molasses have a very strong flavor, so use either molasses or honey, depending on your preference.

Who Knew?

Cinnamon: Did you know that just 1 tsp. (5 mL) contains 28 g of calcium, 1 mg of iron, 1 g of fiber and a lot of Vitamins C, K and manganese? So, add it to anything you bake. Cinnamon has also been shown to lower blood glucose levels, in several studies.

Yield: 36 cookies
Prep Time: 30 minutes

Energy Bars

These bars are a great way to get lots of healthy goodness into your kids and they will love them. The chocolate chips add the sweet kick that allows us to disguise the good stuff that kids don't need to know is in there. Remember: Never tell them what is in there and if they ask ... lie! I know I am going to hell, I'm over it!

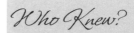
Who Knew?

1 cup	oats	250 mL
¼ cup	wheat flour	60 mL
½ cup	wheat germ	125 mL
½ cup	sunflower seeds	125 mL
½ cup	almonds	125 mL
½ cup	apricots	125 mL
½ cup	dates	125 mL
½ cup	raisins	125 mL
1	scoop protein powder (optional)	1
1 tsp.	cinnamon	5 mL
⅓ cup	100% pure maple syrup	75 mL
2	eggs	2
½ cup	chocolate chips	125 mL

♡ Using a food processor, blend all of the ingredients except the chocolate chips.

♡ Grease a 9" (23 cm) square baking pan. Spread the batter into the pan.

♡ Bake at 350°F (180°C) for 15-20 minutes or until golden brown.

♡ Remove bars from the oven and while still hot, sprinkle the top with the chocolate chips, as they start to melt – spread evenly.

♡ Cut into 12, 2" (5 cm) squares.

Granola Bars: Did you know that a lot of prepackaged granola bars have as much fat and sugar as a commercial chocolate bar with minimal fiber? Most contain chemicals and preservatives to extend the shelf life. Have a look at your kid's favorite lunch time snack and see if you can actually read out loud the ingredients list – if you have a hard time saying any of the words, you can bet your body has a hard time digesting it!

Yield: 12 servings
Prep Time: 1 hour

Chocolate Balls

Who Knew?

Maple Syrup is not just a good natural sweetener but it is high in manganese which gives you energy and has antioxidant properties. It also supports your immune systems.

Make sure you are buying pure maple syrup – don't get fooled by imitations, they are just pure sugar.

These are absolutely delicious plus this is a fast and easy, no-bake recipe!

¾ cup	almond butter (or any nut butter that you would prefer)	175 mL
¼ cup	tahini	60 mL
½ cup	100% pure maple syrup	125 mL
1 cup	toasted sesame seeds*	250 mL
¼ cup	cocoa powder	60 mL
1 cup	oat bran	250 mL
½ cup	wheat germ	125 mL

♡ Add nut butter, tahini and maple syrup to food processor; blend until smooth. Add sesame seeds, cocoa, oat bran and wheat germ; blend until it forms a dough. I find I have to do this part with my hands and knead it all together.

♡ When it is mixed through, roll into balls.

♡ Store in sealed container in the refrigerator for 2 weeks or you can freeze them. But, if you can make them last 2 weeks – e-mail me!

....

* To toast sesame seeds, place them in a dry pan over medium heat and stir continuously until the seeds become light brown in color.

Yield: 32 servings
Prep Time: 20 minutes

Chewy Date Bars

My kids and I have tried the commercial brand of these called "Larabar" and absolutely loved them, until I saw the price. With two growing boys with huge appetites, I decided I could make these myself. Here they are – Enjoy!

Ginger Date Bars
Yield: 24 servings
Serving Size: 1 square,
2" (5 cm)
Prep Time:
30 minutes to soak dates;
30 minutes prep time

GINGER DATE BARS:

1 cup	dates	250 mL
1 cup	almonds	250 mL
½ cup	pecans	125 mL
1 tsp.	powdered ginger	5 mL
1 tsp.	cinnamon	5 mL
¼ tsp.	cloves	1 mL

BANANA DATE BARS:

1 cup	dates	250 mL
1 cup	almonds	150 mL
½ cup	bananas	125 mL

Banana Date Bars
Yield: 16 servings
Serving Size: 2" (5 cm)
square
Prep Time:
30 minutes to soak dates;
30 minutes prep time

CHOCOLATE MOLE DATE BARS:

1 cup	dates	250 mL
¾ cup	almonds	175 mL
½ cup	walnuts	125 mL
¼ cup	cocoa	60 mL
1 tsp.	cinnamon	5 mL
¼ tsp.	cayenne pepper	1 mL

Chocolate Mole Date Bars
Yield: 16 servings
Serving Size:2" (5 cm)
Prep Time:
30 minutes to soak dates;
30 minutes prep time

CASHEW DATE BARS:

1 cup	dates	250 mL
1 cup	cashews	250 mL

PECAN DATE BARS:

1 cup	dates	250 mL
1 cup	almonds	250 mL
½ cup	pecans	125 mL

APPLE PIE BARS:

1 cup	dates	250 mL
1 cup	dried apple chips	250 mL
½ cup	walnuts	125 mL
? cup	raisins	
1 tsp.	cinnamon	

♡ Break apart the dates and place them in a bowl. Pour enough boiling water over the dates to cover them and let sit for about 30 minutes to soften them. Drain the dates.

♡ In a food processor, combine all of the ingredients; blend until finely chopped. Do not purée.

♡ Spread the mixture onto a cookie sheet lined with parchment paper. The batter will be about ¼" (6 mm) thick and will not cover the entire baking sheet. Because the consistency of this batter is very sticky, a helpful hint is to place the batter on a cookie sheet, spread plastic wrap on top of the batter and press it down with your hands to flatten. Don't worry about trying to make it perfectly even, just make the ends as straight as possible.

♡ Bake at 350°F (180°C) for 25 minutes, or until it is no longer sticky on top.

Tofu Chocolate Pudding

The key to this pudding is to not tell your kids what is in it – they will never know!

12 oz.	pkg. soft tofu	340 g
1/3 cup	100% pure maple syrup	75 mL
1/4 cup	cocoa	60 mL
1 tsp.	vanilla	5 mL

♡ In a food processor or blender; combine all ingredients until smooth.

♡ Pour the pudding into plastic containers with lids; and pack into lunch kits! Yummy!

Banana Chocolate Pudding with a Twist!

Again, the key is to NOT *tell your children, what is in the pudding. The avocado has a very mild taste and adds a creamy, smooth texture. This is also an incredible source of omega-3 fat. Yummy and extremely nutritious.*

1	whole ripe avocado	1
4	bananas	4
¼ cup	cocoa	60 mL
1 tbsp.	100% pure maple syrup	15 mL
	water	

♡ In a food processor or blender; blend all of the ingredients. Adjust the sweetness as desired by adding extra maple syrup; and the texture by adding enough water to make a smooth consistency.

♡ This tastes best the day you make it.

Yield: 3 servings
Prep Time: 10 minutes

Applesauce

This is an opportunity to use those tiny crabapples. They make the most lovely pink applesauce.

> crabapples
> water
> honey (optional)
> cinnamon to taste (optional)

♡ Fill a Dutch oven, full of apples. You don't have to peel, core, or de-stem, just throw them in and cover with water.

♡ Bring the apples to a boil, reduce heat and simmer until the skins split and the apples are soft.

♡ With a slotted spoon, remove the apples and push through a food mill. A food mill is a hand-held grinding device, that separates the core and skin from the applesauce. If you don't have a food mill, you can push the apples through a food sieve. You now have applesauce.

♡ Add honey, to taste, depending on the tartness of the apples.

♡ Add cinnamon.

♡ Freeze in plastic containers.

....

Variations:

Pear Sauce: You can use pears as well; or combine crabapples and pears, half and half.

Who Knew?

Apples can help control weight gain, lower the risk of heart disease and fight cancer.

Yield: 40 servings
Serving Size: ½ cup
(125 mL)

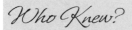

Hazelnuts are an excellent source of vitamin E. They also help in the formation of red blood cells.

Chocolate Hazelnut Spread

This is my healthy version of Nutella. No peanut oil, dairy, refined sugars or trans fats!

⅓ cup	raw hazelnuts, with the skin on	75 mL
¼ cup	100% pure maple syrup	60 mL
2 tbsp.	cocoa	30 mL
	*almond milk, soymilk or water (optional)	

♡ Toast hazelnuts at 400°F (200°C) or in a toaster oven, until the skins are very dark and start to peel off, about 5-10 minutes. Remove; set aside to cool.

♡ When cool, remove the majority of the skin by rubbing the cooled hazelnuts between you hands. Don't worry about getting them completely clean.

♡ In a food processor, process until nuts are similar to grainy butter. Add maple syrup and cocoa; process. Add liquid if the consistency it too thick – you want it to be spreadable like peanut butter.

♡ Store in refrigerator in an airtight container up to 2 weeks (if it lasts that long!)

....

Tip: I make sandwiches with this mixture, spread onto grainy-brown bread with slices of bananas, strawberries or kiwis. The kids devour them!

* If the consistency is too thick, add a little almond milk, soymilk or water

Yield: ½ cup (125 mL)
Prep Time: 20 minutes

Homemade Granola

Great served with yogurt or sprinkled on cereal or fruit salad. I make my kids, breakfast sundaes with this mixture.

7 cups	rolled oat OR rye flakes	1.75 L
3 cups	puffed millet OR rice	750 mL
2 cups	ground flax	500 mL
1 cup	cocoa	250 mL
2 cups	pumpkin seeds	500 mL
1 cup	sunflower seeds	250 mL
1 cup	chopped nuts (your choice)	250 mL
½ cup	canola oil	125 mL
¼ cup	water	60 mL
2 tsp.	vanilla	10 mL
1 tsp.	sea salt	5 mL
1 cup	liquid honey	250 mL
1 cup	raisins	250 mL

♡ In a large bowl, mix together the oats, puffed millet, flax, cocoa, pumpkin seeds, sunflower seeds and your choice of chopped nuts.

♡ In a small saucepan over medium heat, stir together the oil, water, vanilla, sea salt and honey; heat through. Pour over dry mix until completely covered.

♡ Spread onto a cookie sheet and bake at 325°F (160°C). Stir every 5 minutes for at total of 20 minutes.

♡ Stir in the raisins; cook for an additional 5 minutes.

....

Variation:

Breakfast Sundae: Layer granola, yogurt and frozen or fresh berries in a sundae cup. This makes a nice treat for the kids because it tastes like dessert!

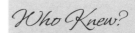
Who Knew?

Pre-packaged Cereals are made with a process called extrusion. They create a slurry and then put it through a machine that makes the shapes. Then they are sprayed with oil and sugar. The process destroys most of the nutrients in the grain. It destroys fatty acids and even destroys the chemical vitamins added at the end. Don't even get me started on the addition of dyes, fat and sugar (high fructose corn syrup). All boxed cereals that are made into shapes or flakes are made this way, even the ones sold in health food stores. Yikes!

Dried Apple Chips

These are delicious and a nice change from the norm.

5 or 6	apples	5 or 6
¼ cup	lime juice	60 mL
¼ cup	water	60 mL
1 tbsp.	sugar	15 mL
	cinnamon and sea salt	

♡ Slice the apples very thin, about ⅛" (3 mm). I use a mandolin (a food slicer) which is very easy and fast, but if you do not have one, use a knife.

♡ In a separate bowl, mix the lime juice, water and sugar. Place the apple slices in enough liquid to cover. Let sit for a few minutes; drain in a colander.

♡ Place apple slices on cooling racks on top of cookie sheets; sprinkle lightly with cinnamon and sea salt.

♡ Bake at 180°F (83°C) for 3 to 4 hours, until crisp. (If you have a dehydrator, use that instead of baking.)

....

Note: Don't be afraid of the sea salt, it adds an incredible flavor.

OTHER SNACK IDEAS:

♡ Homemade popcorn, NOT microwaved (it is full of nasty chemicals).

♡ Nachos and salsa (or salsa with a twist is even better!)

♡ Celery, almond butter and raisins

♡ Celery, sunflower butter and raisins

♡ Celery, cashew butter and raisins

♡ Chocolate covered pretzels

♡ Apple and cheese slices (Please, don't use processed cheese.)

♡ Small container of granola and yogurt, the kids can mix it together at lunchtime, so that it doesn't go soggy.

♡ Cheese and crackers

♡ Fruit and dip

♡ Hard-boiled eggs with a little sea salt

♡ Celery, cream cheese, raisins or craisins

Who Knew?

Microwave Popcorn contains a chemical called diacetyl which gives it the butter flavor and smell. Many studies have shown that this chemical causes lung damage when the bag is opened and the chemical is let out into the air. How about making popcorn the old-fashioned way? It is better tasting and much better for you!

SOURCES

Acid Reflux: page 30, www.medicinenet.com
Apples: page 72, www.essortment.com
Avocados: page 16, www.avocado.org/healthy_living/nutrition.php
Beans: page 36, www.whfoods.com
Beets: page 34, www.whfoods.com
Cabbage: page 42, www.ezlhearticles.com
Cacao Nibs: page 62, www.regainhealthnaturally.com
Chickens: page 58, www.goveg.com/f-top10chickens.asp
Chickpeas: page 18, www.wikipedia.org/wik,/chickpeas
Cocoa, Pure: page 70, www.sciencedaily.com
Coconut Oil: page 25, www.mercola.com
Cranberries: page 53, www.cranberryinstitute.org
Eggs: page 54-55, www.healthdiaries.com
Flax: page 64, www.canadianorganicflax.om
Garbage Free Lunches: page 10, www.wastefreelunches.org/
Garlic: page 22, www.ivillage.co.uk.com
Ginger: page 63, www.letsconnect.com
High Fructose Corn Syrup: page 14,
www.menstuff.org/issues/byissue/highfructose.html#dangers,
Honey: page 32, www.bees-online.com
Hot dogs: pages 56-57, www.ghchealth.com/hot-dogs-question-and answers.html;
www.naturalnews.com/007133.html
Margarine, page 35, Weston A. Price Foundation by Sally Fallon author of *Nourishing Traditions: The Cookbook that Challenges Politically Correct Nutrition* and the *Diet Dictocrat*
Microwave Popcorn: page 76, www.thepumhandle.wordpress.com
Microwaving: page 38, www.helium.com
Organic Foods: page 12, www.ota.com/organic_and_you/10reasons.html ,
www.organicconsumers.org/ or in your local library.
Plastic Water Bottles: page 14, www.greenfeet.net/newsletter/The-dangers-of-plastic-water-bottles.shtml
Pre-packaged Cereals: page 74, Weston A. Price Foundation by Sally Fallon author of the book *Nourishing Traditions*
Sesame Seeds: page 43, www.whafoods.org
Spelt Flour: page 24, www.omafra.gov.on.ca
Sweet Potatoes: page 46, www.whfoods.com/genpage.php?tname=foodspice&dbid=64
The Dangers of Corn Syrup; Dr. Spears *High Speed Fat Loss in 7 Easy Steps,* Published by Al Sears, MD, Copyright 2008 by Wellness Research & Consulting, Inc.
Tomatoes & Lycopene: page 40, www.tomatowellness.com/health.html;
www.ctga.org/newctga/health/studyconfirms.htm
Turmeric: page 44, www.lionsgrip.com
Type 2 Diabetes and High Blood Pressure: page 14,
diabetes.about.com/od/childrenanddiabetes/a/kidsandobesity.htm

INDEX

Index 79

Visit our website at **www.lunchboxlove.ca**

MURDER
MOST
FLORID

MURDER MOST FLORID

INSIDE THE MIND OF A FORENSIC BOTANIST

DR MARK A. SPENCER

Hardie Grant

QUADRILLE

Publishing Director Sarah Lavelle
Editor Susannah Otter
Designer Nikki Ellis
Head of Production Stephen Lang
Production Controller Katie Jarvis

Published in 2019 by Quadrille, an imprint
of Hardie Grant Publishing

Quadrille
52–54 Southwark Street
London SE1 1UN
quadrille.com

Cataloguing in Publication Data: a catalogue
record for this book is available from the
British Library.

text © Dr Mark Spencer 2019
cover photography © Kim Lightbody 2019
design © Quadrille 2019

ISBN 978-1787134003

Printed in Italy

This book is dedicated to the plants and the dead.

Contents

The Phone Call

Sitting at my desk, my eyeballs are gasping for colour and sustenance. The open-plan office is very grey and devoid of natural light. I'm rather bored and don't feel particularly engaged with my work today, which is unusual because I have an amazing job. I am the curator of the British and Irish herbarium at the Natural History Museum in London. An herbarium is a collection of dried plants. It's the sort of job that botanists would clamber over the flailing limbs of their competitors to get to. Nevertheless, I'm bored. It's just one of those days.

The phone rings and I pick it up expecting to speak to a colleague. But it's not a colleague: the voice on the other end of the line is a crime-scene investigator. They ask if I am available to assist them with a potential murder enquiry. The very heavily decayed remains of a man have been found by the edge of a river. He has been identified and is believed to be estranged from his family. There are concerns that he may have been killed by a relative, but it is also known that his mental health was poor, so suicide can't be ruled out. When discovered, the man's body was partially covered by vegetation and the crime-scene investigator would like to know if I can provide an estimate of how old the plants are. They hope this information will help establish how long his remains have been at the location.

As I ask some questions about the vegetation surrounding the body, it soon becomes clear the investigator knows almost nothing about plants.

Equally, I know very little about crime scenes. I can't draw upon television crime dramas for knowledge as I've never been a fan, unless they have Christopher Meloni in them, but that's another matter. The investigator offers to send me some images from the 'deposition scene' and sensing I'm green, she warns me that the images are very graphic. I accept. At least they won't be grey.

She was right, the images are graphic. As the office is open plan, I take care to open the file so that colleagues cannot see what I'm looking at. Luckily, the desk dividers are high and I'm in the darkest corner of the room. No doubt my colleagues can hear my exclamation, but they take no notice; they're used to my intemperate outbursts. The images are of the deposition scene, where the man's body was found. There is lush vegetation along a riverbank, and it looks quite idyllic, except for the partially submerged shopping trolley and the man's very heavily decayed body. He is partially clothed, but his clothing can barely be discerned because it is discoloured by his putrefied remains. His ribcage, spinal column, arms and partially de-fleshed skull are clearly visible. His teeth appear bared. They are not – his lips are no longer there, as they have been consumed by a diversity of organisms feeding on his remains. The nature of the decay is such that what remains of him is either dark charcoal grey or ash coloured and contrasts strongly with the late summer green tones of the vegetation surrounding him. I take in the images and await my reaction; will I be able to withstand this? I feel fine, which is a relief.

I call the crime-scene investigator back, confirming that I can assist and make my arrangements to travel to the deposition scene. Before I leave, I go upstairs to visit colleagues; they are both forensic entomologists. The Natural History Museum is well known for its expertise in dinosaurs, but behind the closed doors are many other specialists who are world experts in their own fields. One large group of researchers and curators are the entomologists. They look after and study the museum's vast collection of insects. My colleagues use information collected from insects to estimate how long a person has been dead; this estimate is known as the post-mortem interval. I need their advice and in return they have a favour to ask. They need me to collect insect larvae from the body and the ground nearby. They explain to me how I need to collect the specimens and how they should be stored. Am I happy to do that? I say yes and they give me some personal protective clothing as I have none. One of them also gives me a little pep-talk; she is very experienced when it comes to working with the dead and has even worked at the body farm in Tennessee, a famous outdoor research facility where the donated bodies of the dead are studied in scenarios emulating murder scenes or disasters.

On my way to the scene, I divert to a chemist and buy some surgical grade soap. I'm not particularly obsessive about hygiene but I'm starting to feel some anxiety about what I'm about to confront. It's a long train journey and I attempt to brace myself for what I'm soon to experience.

On arrival, I make my way to the local police station to meet the police officer in charge of the case, as well as the forensic scientist appointed to oversee my work. The officer explains to me that since my phone conversation the man's remains have been removed. We then proceed to where the body was found. The area is a typical light-industrial corner of a small town on the edge of the Pennines. Behind the single-storey warehouses and lockups, there is a small river edged with surviving fragments of the pre-industrial landscape. Most of the dominant plants are native trees and shrubs but there is also an abundance of invasive non-native Japanese knotweed (*Fallopia japonica*), buddleia (*Buddleja davidii*; confusingly the scientific name is spelt '*Buddleja*' whilst the English names are 'buddleia' or 'butterfly bush') and Himalayan balsam (*Impatiens glandulifera*). There is an officer stationed near the entrance of the site to keep the curious at bay. We climb over the fence and walk forward. Soon we can smell decay.

When we get to the deposition scene, I discover that the police have cut down most of the vegetation and raked it into piles. Not a good start. Estimating the age of vegetation is largely dependent upon its being intact! The police officer removes the tarpaulin that covers the deposition scene. Although they have removed the man's skeleton and personal possessions, a lot of his body tissue and stomach contents remain spread over the adjoining vegetation. The smell is almost overpowering. I try and take in the experience, without appearing inexperienced. The officer accompanying me explains that the police believe that the man's body had been there for several months and that he had been submerged two or three times by floodwater.

The smell is very intense. It is so strong that the officer tells me that, 'This is the worst one I've had in seventeen years.' I resist the urge to tell him this is my first case. In fact, I'm so determined to do the job properly and not appear naïve that I get on my hands and knees and start to examine the decaying flesh attached to the vegetation very carefully. Now, the smell is overpowering and in the back of my mind I can feel the compulsion to retch, but I withstand the urge and proceed with my observations. I am looking at the stems of the Himalayan balsam, or rather I'm looking at the bases of the ones that escaped the strimming. They are flattened against the ground and are partially covered in decayed human tissue. It appears that the man's body was either placed or came to rest on top of the stems. At one point my physiological responses threaten to take control and I feel I may be sick. I stand up and breezily start a conversation with the officer. My strategy works, and the upwelling of nausea subsides, so I get back down on my knees.

After finishing my botanical examination, I explain my findings to the officer, couching them with one major caveat, which is that the strimming and subsequent raking has rather damaged the vegetation – basically, I don't have a lot to go on! However, the man's remains were laid on top of the partially decayed stems of the Himalayan balsam, an invasive non-native species that is an annual. Annual plants usually germinate from seed each spring, grow, flower and set new seed within one year or growing season. For example, the common wild plant, thale cress (*Arabidopsis thaliana*), a small member of the cabbage family (*Brassicaceae*) can complete its life cycle in less than six weeks. Himalayan balsam originates from the foothills of the Himalayas. Each spring after the last frosts, seed in the ground germinates and the young plants rapidly grow to a height of one or two metres before flowering and dropping new seed, until the first frosts of autumn, which kill the adult plant. Owing to its beauty, Himalayan balsam was introduced to British gardens in the 1830s and was established in the wild by the late 1850s. Since then it has spread rapidly because of its fecund nature; a metre-square clump of the plant can produce up to 32,000 seeds. It is particularly abundant by streams and rivers in the cooler parts of these islands.

Based on my knowledge of the ecology, I estimate that the Himalayan balsam plants are about six months old. And it's also possible to estimate when the man's body flattened them. This can be done by examining the regrowth pattern of the remaining stems emerging from beneath his remains. I tell the officer that, based upon my observations, the man arrived at the location within the last two months.

I explain that I'll provide a full report of my findings, but before I go, I need to collect the entomological samples for my colleagues, whose careful instructions I follow to the letter. My colleagues had told me that once fly larvae have finished feeding, they move away from their food source and bury themselves in the ground to pupate. They do this to avoid getting eaten by other animals feeding on the remains. I collect soil samples from around the deposition scene in the hope that there are fly pupae in the samples. I carefully document where and at what depth each sample of soil is taken from. Once I finish collecting the samples, the officer very kindly offers to take me to the storage facility where the man's personal possessions are being held. There are a lot of 'maggots' on his clothing that I can take to supplement the material I've already collected.

We arrive at the anonymous police facility on an industrial estate. I don't know whether it's a reflection of our society's changing attitudes towards policing or tightening budgets, but we now rarely place our police stations at the heart of our towns and cities. Often, they appear to be shoved away in the metaphorical dark corners of our communities. They have become utilities. I'm shown into a room with two or three cabinets designed to dry decayed and wet evidence. The smell is awful. Despite the room having air-conditioning, the stench is magnified and much more intense than outdoors. As I open the door to the drying cabinet, a wall of odour like burnt car tyres mixed with intense sweet sickly jasmine, assails me. The smell is partially made up of 3-methylindole, also known as skatole. Skatole and the related chemical indole, along with putrescine and cadaverine, are produced during decomposition of animal bodies. The officer backs out of the room and leaves me to it.

In front of me are the last of the man's personal possessions; his badly stained clothing is barely recognisable as garments. The fold and curve of his now absent torso and limbs are picked out by the staining. It's very sad. For some reason it reminds me of the Shroud of Turin – I don't know why, I'm not a religious man. I take hold of a pair of tweezers and start removing larvae and pupae from the clothing. They are quite hard to see so I need to get very close to the fabric to remove them and because of this, the smell intensifies as I drop the insects into sample vials. It's not an ammonia-like smell, my eyes don't water, but it is hammering into my nasal cavity; it feels like I am inhaling dense, liquid odour. Once I have collected the entomological samples I stand up, close the cabinet and gratefully retreat for fresh air. The officer hastily closes the door to the room, and I take my leave.

As I head home, I feel very emotionally charged. I keep smelling rich jasmine-rubbery odours coming off me. I go into a train-station toilet and wash my hands vigorously with the surgical soap I bought earlier. Still, the smell remains. I'm also feeling slightly nauseous. I tell myself that this is largely an evolutionary response and that it's natural to feel this way; the gag reflex evolved to ensure we eject toxic material and minimise potential harm. Nevertheless, I feel I need to tackle the sensation, and I'm hungry. For some curious reason, I decide I need to find a food that is some way emblematic of the decay I've just experienced. Short on options, I choose a potato salad, rich and runny with mayonnaise. I then get on the train and head home. I eat my meal very slowly and carefully, each mouthful accompanied by a swirl of thoughts and emotions.

The smell continues to linger in my mind. Several days later, despite having showered and changed clothes, I can still smell that rich, cloying scent of decay. I know there's nothing there, but I catch myself sniffing my forearms just in case I've missed a bit. My mind keeps running through my experience by the riverbank and I check that my conclusions are sound. I have a residual fear that I have missed something or that my observations are not correct. Could I do this again? Would I like to? Yes, I'm hooked already – it's fascinating. Now, every time the phone rings in my office, I have a flutter of anticipation. *Is it another case?*

1
Botany, Forensics and Me

It's almost a decade since I forced myself to eat that potato salad. A lot has happened since. I no longer work for the Natural History Museum. I departed the caring arms of the mothership and decided to brave the world on my own. I have what is euphemistically called a portfolio career. A friend told me that's what panicking about the mortgage and hovering over the emails, waiting for business, is called nowadays. I now call myself a forensic botanist, although that does not cover all that I do. I'm also a hired entertainer, a public speaker, aiming to enthuse people about the world of plants. Where I can, I also try to continue some of the botanical research that interests me.

Usually, the first reaction when I introduce myself is 'forensic what?' Sometimes there might be a bit of tittering around the word 'botany' – the *Carry On* gene is never very far away in the British psyche. Many people have not heard of botany and if they have, they think it's another word for gardening. Botany is not gardening, although gardening quite often relies upon knowledge originating from the research of botanists. In fact, botany is arguably the oldest scientific discipline. Humanity has been examining, describing and trying to understand plants and fungi since antiquity. Until the early sixteenth century, most European knowledge about plants was based upon the work of ancient Greeks such as Theophrastus and Dioscorides, and much of this knowledge was intertwined with medicine.

From about 1550 the modern science of botany evolved rapidly, and now takes in all aspects of the life of plants, their morphology, anatomy, physiology, ecology, genetics, classification and evolution. Traditionally, botany also included the study of fungal organisms. Today, because of our increased understanding of the major biological differences between plants and fungi, the study of fungi is a separate discipline and is given its own name – mycology. These differences often surprise people, but what is even more surprising to many is that fungi are more closely related to us than they are to plants. Animals and fungi are opisthokonts. The word opisthokont refers to similarities in the cell structure and chemistry of both groups.

I appreciate that some non-scientists often feel confused or daunted by scientific names, but they do get easier with a little perseverance. In many cases you're using them without realising they're scientific. Familiar garden plant names like geranium, eucalyptus, chrysanthemum and fuchsia are all scientific in origin. Similarly, every time you say octopus or hippopotamus, you're using scientific names. In themselves, scientific names are not important, they are gateways to information. I know this sounds counter-intuitive, especially from a scientist. But a name is essentially an aide-mémoire that accesses the important information that relates to the object in question. Thus, in the case of the common lawn daisy, its universally accepted scientific name, *Bellis perennis*, was first published by Carl Linnaeus in 1753. In itself, the scientific name is not a vital piece of information, but it leads us to all the published science that has been written about that plant over the last two and a half centuries. The use of a universal name for organisms reduces the potential for confusion. This name is called the binomial. A binomial is made up of two parts, the genus (*Bellis*) and the species (*perennis*). Essentially, the genus is the collective noun for a grouping of closely related species. In the case of *Bellis*, there are other daisy species, such as *Bellis annua* and *Bellis sylvestris*. To save space, botanists often abbreviate the genus name, in this case to, '*B.*'. To see *B. annua* and *B. sylvestris* growing wild you'll have to go to southern Europe and the Mediterranean as they do not occur on these shores.

A binomial allows a fellow scientist, or expert witness or jury, to have a high confidence that what I am discussing is comparable to their understanding, that it has verifiability. We humans apply the concept of naming (nomenclature) to many, many things in our world. The naming of elements and compounds in chemistry is a form of nomenclature. One of the objectives of this book is to give the reader an insight into the world of forensic botany, and the application of scientific names is part of that. In presenting my observations on a plant or a plant fragment I need to be able to convey what I think it is, as well as validate my conclusions, and this can only easily be done via the name.

I could choose to use only the English vernacular name for the plants discussed. But, unfortunately, while many plants have a standard English name, some do not. More problematically, there is a great variation in which English names are used. A classic example is 'bluebell'. In England this is traditionally applied to *Hyacinthoides non-scripta* and in Scotland, harebell, *Campanula rotundifolia* formerly bore the name. Some of our wild plants can have dozens of regional name variations. Cleavers (*Galium aparine*), is an annual plant that is common across our lowlands and it bears a host of now largely forgotten names – bobby buttons, catchweed, claggy meggies, gollen weed, goosegrass, herriff, sticky bob, robin-run-the-hedge and sticky willy are a small selection of those names. Generally, scientific names are much less prone to this level of variation.

By convention, scientific plant names are italicised; the main reason for this is that the name stands out on the page. You will also notice that sometimes I use the abbreviation 'spp.', which simply means more than one species of plant (e.g. *Acer* spp. will refer to two or more species of *Acer*). On occasion, I will also mention plant families. Like genus, the family can be thought of as a collective noun. In this case, a collective noun for related genera (the plural of genus). For example, in the mint family (*Lamiaceae*), there are many genera including sage (*Salvia*), lavender (*Lavandula*), thyme (*Thymus*) and marjoram (*Origanum*). Even a brief list like this can convey more meaning than merely the identity of the plants themselves. If I were presented with this list and asked to say where in the world this group of plants originated from, I would suggest the Mediterranean. These plants are classic indicators of the Mediterranean and are typically found in aromatic and thorny shrubland in sunny locations that are seasonally hot and dry.

The idea that plants can help fight crime causes much surprise and some confusion in most people, even the police. In many cases, people think that my work involves studying plants that can be used to poison people. On occasion I do examine poisonous plants, but not that often. Recently, I met someone who assumed that being a forensic botanist meant that I was particularly careful in my critique of urban land management practices. In the context of what we were discussing, it was a reasonable assumption, but the suggestion did rather take me by surprise. My work as a forensic botanist largely focuses on helping to reveal how and when serious crimes such as murder occurred. Plants and other organisms react to the presence of the dead, they grow around human remains and can become time capsules enshrouding the person and bearing tell-tale signs of what happened. My work also involves searching for the dead. Some of the work I do is on 'cold cases' in which I aim to help the police find murder victims hidden in our landscape. Plants, and other aspects of the landscape, can be used to help locate missing or murdered people. Burying victims in woodland leaves a trace, even after several years. Finally, using trace evidence from the environment, especially leaf and fruit fragments, I help to link suspects to crime scenes or victims. As people move about, they come into contact with plants. Fragments of plants (and other trace evidence such as fibres, soil, insects) become attached to suspects, their possessions or their victims. Each fragment can lead to a better understanding of how a crime was committed.

Forensic botany is not a discipline that works best in isolation. It is part of a wider sphere of forensic work known as environmental forensics, a catch-all term that refers to any material from the natural world that can be used forensically. Data derived from soil, insects, animals, plants and fungi all qualify as environmental. Building an understanding of how a crime can leave traces in the environment is challenging and complex. New areas of scientific research exploring the chemistry of decay and diversity of the microbial world offer exciting new opportunities for using environmental forensics in the courtroom. I'll explore this in more detail later.

As engaging as the typical television crime dramas are, they are poor reflections of reality. In arguably the most famous of these series, *CSI: Crime Scene Investigation*, the viewer is often treated to the main character, Gil Grissom, solving the case using his nimble mind and mastery of several unrelated scientific disciplines. He's a forensic entomologist, but he also appears to be a dab hand at criminal psychology, fingerprinting, DNA analysis and gunshot residue, among other things. Sadly, most of us are really not that gifted, and if you encounter a forensics specialist who claims to have such a wide scope of abilities, I would advise you to be very sceptical indeed. In many cases, it can take years to fully hone your skills in any one aspect of the forensic environment. On screen, the aura of scientific brilliance and geekery is enhanced by snazzy computer facilities, mysterious machines that whirl and multicoloured test tubes. And lab coats. If you're clever, you've got to have a lab coat. And, it will be pristine. When I was doing my PhD, my lab coat always looked like I'd just dug up this season's potatoes. Yes, there may be some modern technology available but often it is as simple as careful observation and a good-quality microscope. Television programmes focusing on the high-tech often lead the viewer to believe that crimes are solved in the blink of an eye using gadgets. Usually, they are not. Often the work is time consuming and is based upon long-established techniques and a thorough understanding of a scientific area of study. In my case, plants.

For the first forty-plus years of my life I never conceived that my love of plants would take me on this journey. I never considered that plants and I could play a part in understanding how the act of committing a crime unfolds or that my knowledge could help bring comfort to the families and friends of the deceased.

Not surprisingly, confidentiality is paramount. It is amazing how some people try and wheedle information out of you. I am very cautious, having once been duped by a journalist (on a matter unrelated to forensics) when I worked for the Natural History Museum. Now, I have become quite adept at talking expansively without saying anything substantive about my work! Knowing what has happened to someone long before a case has gone to court is a strange experience, as is seeing it on the news and knowing some of the 'truth'! This leads me to needing to disappoint; if you are reading this book in the hope of finding out something exciting about a case you've seen on television, you'll need to head towards the internet. While I have drawn upon cases I have worked on and in parts directly referenced some of them, I have left out key pieces of information relating to names and locations. Also, I have not fully described real examples of evidence. To do so would cause harm to my professional reputation and could affect the outcome of an investigation. Indeed, some of the cases I have been involved with are still ongoing, particularly missing person searches. Even for those that have gone to trial there is always the possibility that an appeal may be launched. Most importantly to me, it must be awful to be reminded of your loss if you're the friend or relative of someone who has died under these circumstances. Therefore, when talking or writing about the work I do, I endeavour to ensure the anonymity of the cases I have worked on. I have a creeping dread of being held to account by an audience member (or reader) announcing that I have just been discussing the death of someone they love. I know it's unlikely, but it could happen. Where appropriate, I have drawn upon publicly documented cases that I have not worked upon to illustrate the points I am making or to explore techniques that I have not used or am not professionally competent to use. For example, I will discuss the role of forensic botany during the investigation of the murder of the son of the pioneer aviator Charles Lindbergh in the 1930s and the murder of Joanne Nelson in Hull, Yorkshire in 2004.

After my first case, I had to learn quickly about how criminal investigations were managed and structured. I soon discovered that there is a complex ecology of people working with different mindsets and power infrastructures. I had to learn the behaviours and foibles of each new police force and crime-scene team when I met them. I expect they had to do the same thing with me: they were probably wondering 'what's that flower bloke doing?'.

Broadly speaking, most forces arrange their teams in the following manner. Crimes scenes are usually overseen by crime-scene managers (CSMs), who supervise a team of crime-scene investigators (CSIs); these are also known in some forces as scene of crime officers (SOCOs). Their role is to secure and manage the crime scene. Some will have specialisms in specific areas of forensics, but generally their role is to identify, record and recover forensic evidence from crime scenes. As the Nottinghamshire Police website says, 'Unlike CSI: Miami, CSIs in Nottinghamshire do not analyse evidence themselves or arrest criminals!'. CSMs are the police staff I most closely work with.

Alongside the CSI team are the police search advisors (PolSAs). They and their team are warranted officers. I can't help myself here, but I must be a little cheeky: these people are often the tough ones in the team. I say this with respect, as they do a very hard job. It is often these people you'll see on television conducting searches. They must be tough, both in mind as well as in body. Some of them are built like bulldozers and clearly could snap me in half with ease. Needless to say, I'll often find myself gravitating to the ones with broken noses. They're also usually quite a lot of fun! Being on a crime scene can be exhausting and depressing, and sometimes a breath of levity is most certainly needed.

Most of the time it is the PolSAs and the CSIs and CSMs that I work with. The detectives tend to come and go. This is not due to a lack of commitment but because they often must be elsewhere. Sometimes there will be more than one crime scene in an investigation, or they may need to interview witnesses or suspects; and they're often also working on other cases. Overall, I've found that detectives seem to be the most stressed and at times, frankly, rather irascible members of the team. I don't think it's necessarily a character flaw, because their work is stressful. I'd be bloody awful at it. Not the sleuthy part, but the bit where you must deal with murderers and are then expected to be even-handed and professional in meetings. It's a lot to balance.

Far away from the crime scene, back at headquarters, are the forensic submissions staff. These are the people who approve expenditure. In nearly every organisation anyone with this role is rarely the most popular member of staff, and, in my experience, this is also true with the police. On occasion I find myself sharing those feelings; it seems that approval for expenditure gets sucked into a morass while the clock ticks. And, for me and other biologists working in forensics, time is our enemy. The longer a scene or an exhibit is left, the greater the chance that living or dead biological material will change, degrade or be lost. People in centrally heated offices tend to forget that outdoors, seasons change and so do the plants and animals that inhabit a crime scene. This can seriously affect the potential to retrieve relevant biological data. In one case, I have waited over eighteen months to be called to a crime scene to undertake a botany survey. Conducting one can be relatively simple: I make a list of the plants present at a crime scene. Surveys are very important because they are the foundation on which I can compare plant fragments retrieved from exhibits with what is present at a crime scene. Critically, non-botanists often don't realise that many plants are highly seasonal; they'll be easy to see in spring and impossible in the autumn. So, if I am obliged to wait six or more months to do a survey, my job gets a lot harder.

Working alongside the police forces are specialists from forensic service providers (FSPs). This is policy and management speak for commercial companies that provide specialist skills the police either do not have in-house or are unable to deploy owing to resource limitations. On occasion, police forces may not be able to deploy their own specialists to a crime scene if their staff are already committed elsewhere. The police are then obliged to purchase these specialist services from the FSPs. I am on call to work as a subcontractor for the FSPs if they need my expertise. I don't know of an FSP that employs their own forensic botanist; we are quite niche! My work as a forensic botanist means that I am also an expert witness and, if necessary, I attend court to explain my work and my conclusions.

2

The Deposition Scene

It's February, and almost a year after my first case. I'm huddled in the back of a cramped police car and as we negotiate our way through dense urban traffic, all I can see through the rain-spattered windows are the red and orange rear lights of the vehicles in front of us. Periodically, we are blinded by those awful LED headlights of the oncoming cars. The previous day, I was working in the museum, when my desk phone rang. The caller told me that a man's remains had been found on a small piece of derelict land carved out over the decades by the creation of a canal, railway and bypass. The police urgently need to establish how long his remains have been at the deposition scene. Depositions may be due to accidental death, natural death, suicide or by a someone murdering them at the scene or transporting the body to that location. Unsurprisingly, graves always involve third parties.

As we drive to the scene, the crime-scene manager explains the background to the case and how the person was found. Finally, after about twenty minutes we pull over onto the hard shoulder of the trunk road. In front of us, two further police vehicles are parked. As we get out of the car, I prepare myself for meeting the people working on the case. I always slightly dread introductions since I have a horrible memory for people's names and tend to forget them with great rapidity. Sometimes I try and deflate this fear by making a feeble joke about wishing the person was a plant or a fungus, because I'd remember their name then. This is certainly not the time for feeble jokes, so I try and look intelligent and attentive. This is not too hard, it's fairly dark and spitting with rain, and we can't see too much of each other as we gather for another briefing. For the third time, I listen to someone explain the background of the case, this time it's a detective. After almost a year of forensic casework, I've almost learnt to appear less impatient than I really am. Repetition can be useful. It drives home information and as I've discovered, serious crime investigations are conducted by sub-groups of people with their own hierarchies and decision-making processes. It's vital that each of these – forensic service providers, crime-scene managers, police search advisors and the detectives – are all aware of what is known and what is planned. To a new boy like me, this can be confusing. Who calls the shots? I try to appear self-assured and avoid stumbling over the acronyms.

Before we enter the triangle of derelict land, we are required to endure the health and safety talk. This is delivered by one of the PolSA team, who informs us that there is a very steep embankment leading to the deposition scene and that some of the ground is boggy. I groan to myself and in my mind sarcastically thank the officer for telling us about mud! It's a bit like telling a gardener that roses have thorns. The PolSA continues: there is a lot of traffic because there are big roads nearby, don't walk into them. Internally, I feel another shudder of sarcasm. To ram home my pain, the PolSA seems to devote especial attention in explaining all of this to me personally. I suspect that he thinks because I'm not big and burly that somehow I'm delicate, which I most certainly am not. I respond by merrily explaining that we botanists are very much used to this sort of terrain. There's nothing we like more than a patch of marsh to go squelching around in. I've even been known to strip to my underpants when exploring a particularly fascinating wetland. I spare the PolSA that detail.

The slope is indeed very steep and rather slippery. Coming down the slope with me is a woman who will become very important to me in my future work. Her name is Sophie and she works as a forensic anthropologist. The need to study human bones as part of the development of modern medicine has resulted in the creation of many discrete disciplines. Of these disciplines, forensic anthropology was developed to understand the effects of human (and sometimes non-human) activity on the remains of the dead. Forensic anthropologists are very often called to crime scenes, but their work is not limited to that. Accidental deaths or suicide investigations may also require their skills. As we walk along, Sophie presses the CSM on the details of the case. She wants to know more about the circumstances surrounding the discovery of the body. She also asks if the remains have been disturbed since the discovery. I can tell by the look in her eye that she won't be pleased if they have. Sophie is quite curt, and I sense that she is respected. Straight away, I rather like her. Her swift, no-nonsense approach appeals. She isn't bullish but I can see that her directness is intimidating to some. I find it refreshing, and I can understand what drives her to this. People have a horrible tendency to dither when in a group, but Sophie wants and needs to get things moving. This is not merely impatience. There are many reasons why rapid, measured action is needed, the most important being that the remains need to be retrieved and secured.

The CSM explains that the police don't know for certain who the person is, but they believe that the bones may be those of a man who disappeared a decade earlier. There is still enough light to see the ground and the vegetation reasonably clearly. Still standing from the previous summer, the skeletal remains of last year's flower stems hang on. The worn-ivory radiating, symmetrical stems of cow parsley (*Anthriscus sylvestris*) stand out against the drab browns and greens of decaying nettle (*Urtica dioica*), cock's-foot (*Dactylis glomerata*) and bramble (*Rubus* spp.) stems. As we walk forward, the vegetation fades away; we are now beneath a fly-over and the ground is almost entirely bare; hardly a drop of rain has touched here in years. What was once a flower-rich field in a river valley is now cracked clay covered with a dusting of dry tree leaves and litter blown down from the nearby roads. There are signs of rough sleeping amongst the smashed-up and burnt-out remains of domestic rubbish and vehicle parts. Teenagers have been having fun.

Someone has already created a common entry path. The aim of common entry paths is to minimise disturbance and preserve evidence. Despite our best efforts, we humans are rather predictable. Imagine you've committed a crime; it's the depths of night and you need to move quickly to avoid discovery. Nearly all of us would follow in the footsteps of others, using existing paths. As a result, for at least part of their route, criminals tend to stick to paths already created by dog walkers and those who enjoy the countryside. It is here that the investigation needs to preserve evidence. The aim of a well-planned common entry path is to plan a route to the scene that does not appear to have been disturbed by human activity. This should ensure that any evidence remains intact.

As we get nearer to the deposition scene it becomes understandable why the man's remains were missed, despite there being evidence of recent human activity all around. His bones are partially engulfed in brambles, nettles and mosses. Most of his weather-worn and degraded clothing has taken on the palette of the plants around him. Only his skull can be clearly seen, and even that only when we are almost standing on top of his remains.

Sophie and I start to look in more detail at the deposition scene, being careful not to touch anything yet. The first thing we need to do is establish roughly where in the undergrowth his remains are; it's becoming quite hard to see in the now failing light. It's also starting to get rather chilly, the wind is picking up and there are flakes of sleety snow in the air. Sophie asks me what I think, no doubt gently testing the scope of my abilities. To me, it looks like his remains have been here for a long time, several years at least. Young sycamore (*Acer pseudoplatanus*) and ash (*Fraxinus excelsior*) saplings are scattered around the area and several are growing very close to the skeleton. Most appear to be several years old. The brambles that are enshrouding his remains also appear to be about the same age. He has been there a long time, largely alone except for the occasional pyromaniac teenager gang and exhausted rough sleeper.

After an hour spent examining the scene, we retreat up the embankment to discuss how to proceed. By now it is almost dusk, and the weather is becoming quite unpleasant. The temperature has dropped, and icy darts of rain sting our faces. Sophie and I present our initial observations to the

CSM and the PolSAs. The detectives have already departed. By now I know this tends to happen quite often – they've always got places to go. We all agree what actions should be taken next. The most important thing is to secure the scene overnight, which means that some unfortunate junior police officers are going to have to spend the night ensuring that nothing is disturbed by either the curious or the criminal. And, even though the man's remains have lain under the stars for years, we need to erect tents to provide additional cover and reduce the chance of interference.

The PolSA team are sent down to erect the tents and secure the ropes with sandbags or anything weighty that comes to hand, and to set up lighting. The weather is now vile. Whilst this is happening, I explore the nearby vegetation, partially out of general curiosity but also to try to get an understanding of what vegetation management has been undertaken over the last few years. Understanding this will make interpreting the deposition scene easier. On closer inspection, many of the sycamore and ash saplings are older than they initially appeared. Their apparent youth being caused by their having been felled in the past and then regrown. Most of the regrowth appears to be less than ten years old. Sophie focuses on making notes on the position and condition of the remains. I join her, partially because I'm curious to learn more and because I need to take a closer look at the vegetation growing around and through the remains. By this time, metal tread plates have been laid along parts of the common entry path and around the deposition scene. These spread our weight and should prevent damage to any undiscovered evidence underfoot.

Sophie is very keen to see if she can see any signs of damage to the bones. No flesh remains and there is only the lightest whiff of decay, even when our noses are in close proximity to the bones. She is unable to see any signs of damage or trauma to the bones that may indicate violence. However, in this light and late hour she is unwilling to commence a full recovery and documentation. Sophie will need several hours to document the position of the bones and any personal effects that remain. I will also need to map the position of the main vegetation features around the remains as well as examine them more closely. Sophie will then lead on recovering the man's remains and personal effects. Each one will have to be photographed before being placed into evidence bags, or for the larger objects, boxes. We will have to return tomorrow. Once more, we trudge up the slope; by now because of the heavy footfall and the fading light it is starting to get a little treacherous. At the top, Sophie briefs the CSM. Our overall conclusion is that the man's remains appear to have been there for many years, probably up to a decade.

Forensics is certainly not all glamour and, by the end of the day, we are muddy and tired. We have been booked into a nearby hotel. It's one of those typical roadside jobs, and is sufficient. On arrival at the hotel, Sophie and I retire to our rooms and have a quick brush up, and we then return downstairs for a late supper. Among my friends and family, one of my more famed attributes is my enthusiasm for food. Despite my slender frame, I have the appetite of a Roman emperor. I like food and I like a lot of it! I order my meal, which on arrival is rather disappointing. Sophie is keen to talk through the case and our observations. Over the years, I have come to know that this is very typical of her. She can work for hours. Quite often I'll find that if we are on a two or three-day job she'll have worked into the small hours compiling her notes or dealing with tasks relating to other cases she's working on. I can't do that; I really need my sleep! Even though we are quite different in some respects – she's a married mother with a young son, I'm a gay man with no dependents (apart from my long-suffering partner) – we are alike in some respects. We both find people rather annoying at times. Our patience is largely reserved for plants or the dead. I'm deeply grateful for the informal mentoring Sophie has given me over the years. I have not trained formally in forensics, but If I were to be starting afresh, I certainly would consider doing one of the forensic science courses which are now increasingly available. My experience of entering forensics rather late in my career has been fascinating, but some formal training would have eased the transition. I have been very fortunate to have the support of experienced people like Sophie who have guided me through my career and have taught me so much. Her extensive experience of working in a police force and more recently, her years in the private sector, have been invaluable in helping me develop professionally. Over the years, I have never heard her speak blithely or with disregard for any of the deceased that we've work with. She speaks with a tone of fondness and an appreciation that what she does matters.

Talking about murder and decaying bodies around the dinner table in a restaurant is rather odd. It also requires quite a bit of care and discretion. We talk in hushed tones and euphemisms, our eyes occasionally darting around the room to see if anyone has overheard us. As we're talking, Sophie's phone rings and she answers. I listen to the hmms, yeses and okays, and eat my rather awful garlic mushrooms. How is it possible to wreck garlic mushrooms! When the call ends, Sophie looks concerned and tells me that the senior officers overseeing the case want to meet us the following morning. We are to go to the main police station. We have been summoned. We suspect it is because our conclusions do not sit well with their expectations. Time for bed: we'll need fresh heads in the morning.

As I ready myself for sleep, I run through my observations and conclusions, hoping that I've not overlooked something, and fretting that I might have made a fool of myself. As I close my eyes, my brain fills with images of leaf litter, dead stems and bones; I drift off to sleep.

I'm not at my best in the morning and being in an airless hotel room that a close friend would describe as 'worm-medicine' coloured, does not improve me. I stagger down to breakfast and drink as much coffee as my system can take. Half an hour later, we are in a meeting room in the police station. The furniture is worn and stained. As much as television crime dramas try to emulate the full gloom of the average British police station, they never quite achieve it. They are generally damnable places. Those of us who grumble about the public sector and the quality of our policing should be compelled to spend a month working in a local police station, ideally mopping floors, with a toothbrush. I recently visited a major police station in one of our larger cities, where, despite being of recent construction, there were signs of dilapidation. In the basement there was a charming sign asking visitors not to feed the local rat population and my host warned me that the lift lights regularly failed.

As we wait for the meeting to start, sitting on the faintly smelly furniture, several detectives and senior officers walk in and sit down. I wouldn't quite describe the atmosphere as hostile, but they don't appear overly happy to be attending the meeting, nor do some of them seem too pleased to see us. Quietly, Sophie asks me if I'm okay. I reply, 'yes', which is true.

One of the detectives is steadily eyeballing me. He's in his early fifties and is clearly an experienced officer who appears thoroughly sick of his job and no doubt has little time for distractions. I can sense his antipathy. I can't be sure it's not homophobia, but I've seen that look before. Having confronted homophobes and racists on the streets of London in my past, I'm not too concerned, just a little irritated. I can see where this is going and I'm going to have to nip it in the bud. The meeting starts and the most senior officer introduces himself and then introduces the other people in the room. Sophie then commences to summarise our actions to date and offers our initial observations – that the man's remains appear to have been there for many years, probably up to a decade. She then turns to me to explain my own conclusions; the eyes of the boss flicker over me, he thanks her and invites me to proceed.

I quickly decide it's time to assert myself, without appearing rude and aggressive. I also don't want to expose Sophie to criticism, because these are people she knows. I take the plunge. I explain that before I proceed with the botanical science, I feel it's important to explain that, while I may appear to be an ivory-tower academic from London I have a great deal of experience of the plant life of these isles, I have 'real-life experience' (whatever that means!). Even though I'm addressing their boss, I'm carefully standing my ground against some of the people in the room, particularly he who's been continuously eyeballing me. After my brief speech, the senior officer smiles and thanks me for my candour and asks me to proceed. Several detectives slump back in their chairs and reluctantly start listening to me, including the eyeballer.

I start by saying that my observations are provisional. I will fully present my findings after we've completed our examination and documentation of the scene and I have checked my samples back at the museum. Even at this point in my career in forensics, I have learnt not to offer final conclusions until I am confident that I have done all I need do to substantiate them. Resuming, I explain that there is evidence that the vegetation surrounding the man is at least six years old, probably older. I outline how it is possible to make a rough estimate of the age of the saplings by carefully studying their branching patterns and the scars left by leaf buds. I also outline some of my observations relating to the brambles surrounding the remains, which lead me to conclude that the man has been there for quite some time. It simply would not be possible for the plants to grow in the manner they had if the man's remains had arrived there more recently. I sense that the detectives are slowly becoming more interested. They start asking me the odd question. They seem genuinely surprised that 'flowers' could help establish how long undiscovered remains had lain on open ground. The meeting then moves on to how the work will proceed, after which Sophie and I head back to the scene.

When we arrive there, all is in turmoil. Overnight, the wind picked up and flung one of the tents against the fencing of the nearby railway, while the other one is crumpled on the ground. An officer who was on overnight duty explains that they had done their best to prevent further chaos, but the wind had been too strong. We spend half an hour or so helping the PolSAs put everything back in order. Sophie and I then resume our task of documenting the scene and retrieving the man's remains.

First, Sophie and I carefully extract the man's skull from the embracing vegetation, and she examines it carefully, looking for signs of damage. Skulls are beautiful things and holding one is a deeply intimate experience. I briefly hold it to see if there is any information to be had from the attached vegetation. Apart from a thin sheen of green algae growing on the surface, facing upwards towards the rain and sunlight, there is little to observe. A small stem of common ivy (*Hedera helix*) had attached itself to the skull and left behind a few fibrous rootlets. There are two or three tiny wisps of moss attached. All in all, they only confirm that the skull has been there for at least one growing season. We need more information.

I gently pass the skull back to Sophie, who carefully places it in a box, closes the lid and writes some notes in her book and on the box. It is then carried away and locked inside a police vehicle. Slowly, as we start to remove the layers of loose leaf-litter, twigs and sprays of moss, the man's skeletal vertebrae, ribs and upper arms are exposed. Most of his clothing has decayed, although some fragments of trouser pockets and waistband, belt, jacket and shirt cuff and collar remain. We find personal items as we proceed. Everything is recorded and placed in boxes or bags. As we remove the loose vegetation and personal items that are retrievable, we are hampered by the plant growth through the remains. I am keen to retain as much of the lower stems and roots as possible, but we need to take the upper portions away to allow Sophie to do her work. I pull out my secateurs and start pruning. This feels like quite an odd operation to be doing whilst I'm manoeuvring around bones. Somehow, I feel slightly ridiculous and superfluous. I finish my gardening, compile my notes and wait for Sophie to remove the remains so that I can proceed with examining and removing the roots and lower stems of the plants that have grown through and over the remains. Most of the plants I retrieve are brambles. I make a note of how old I estimate each one of them to be and retain some for further examination. At this point it's mid-afternoon and, we have been at the scene for several hours, mainly on our hands and knees. It's not as cold as it was and the sleet has stopped, but we need a rest. Once more, we head up the embankment for a 'brew', a sandwich and a bar of chocolate. As I have come to discover, by police standards this is a good meal. Many of them have terrible diets while on the job! After 15 minutes our late lunch is gone, and we head back down the increasingly slippery slope.

Sophie resumes carefully measuring and documenting the scene. She has laid a long tape measure across the site, from which all further measurements will be taken. The main features of the area – such as the larger trees, the positions of debris like car tyres and, of course, the position of the man's bones are noted and are drawn onto a scale plan that will later be digitally plotted for use in reports. I start cutting down a few saplings, as I want to take back a few stem samples to take a further look at and confirm their age. By dusk, our work is complete, and I head for the train station and home. Once back in London, I need to make a detour to the museum to deposit my samples in a secure store. I have no desire to lose them or have them stolen. I'm home by about 11 pm and head straight to bed. My knees hurt.

3

Becoming a Forensic Botanist

Being in the presence of the dead is an intense experience. Sometimes, I am called to a crime scene soon after the person has been discovered. As a result, I witness what remains of the last moments of a person's life. In the initial stages of an investigation it is sometimes not known how a person died or how they came to be where they are. Their remains are often a testament to what befell them. I have seen the bodies of people who have committed suicide where they are either lying down or partially sitting up apparently taking their last look at this world. Other remains speak of the haphazard nature of life, of unfortunate people who fall to their death or are victims of motoring accidents. The damaged bones and brutalised remains of victims of violence portray the nature of their death. Their remains often appear to encapsulate their state of mind in the moments leading to their death. I can clearly recall the terrorised tension in the decayed limbs of a young woman who had been raped and then murdered. She lay lonely in a ditch, with autumn leaves blown over her, the leaves providing her with dignity in death.

Inevitably and understandably, I often get asked 'how do you cope?'. Generally, I feel 'fine' – very British! This is not a denial of what I have experienced, quite the opposite. People often wonder how I separate myself emotionally from the details of the crime. So far in my career, I have done the opposite. I don't disassociate from the victims: I feel quite engaged with them, even if I can never know what they were really like. I feel very connected to the person and want to learn more about them. I care very much about them, and their family and friends. Having said that, I don't become anxious about playing my part in solving the case; my emotions are largely reserved for making sure I do a good job and don't make any mistakes. Sometimes, when I am involved with searches, it is frustrating not to be able to find someone. But it is important to accept that investigations are very reliant on a wide range of expert disciplines and the accuracy of witness statements. Get one piece of the puzzle wrong and it can be very hard to locate someone. I do feel sad when I travel through certain parts of the country knowing that a victim is out there, possibly within eyesight. Quite often, I familiarise myself with the background to a new case on the internet. My efforts tend not to focus on what the journalists are reporting but go towards researching the local environment and plants. Sometimes this is useful information for me but sometimes it is simple human curiosity. I am most definitely not one of those people that gawps at car crashes on motorways but it does help to learn as much about the case as possible beforehand.

For me, there is no horror in decaying flesh and skeletal remains. The horror is in the minds of the perpetrators; they are the ones who must try to sleep at night and are bound to relive what they have done. The remains of the dead are extraordinarily beautiful and complex. Ironically, they are a hub of life. The biology of decay is incredibly intricate and offers many avenues of research for forensic science. I am not so foolhardy to believe that I will always be fine. Sooner or later I am likely to find what I do very hard to deal with. But, it's worth it. Being part of a community of people doing their best to serve justice for the dead and bring a degree of peace for the living is an honour. So far in my career I have only occasionally felt that flutter of emotional disturbance: one victim bore a striking resemblance to a family member which was very unsettling.

I am also very lucky that I can escape and decompress, because I only do this part time. Being close to the people who do this full time and have done so for years is revealing. Some certainly bear the scars emotionally and a few are quite angry that our society does not really appreciate them. It is very gruelling work, physically and mentally. Some of my friends and family were particularly freaked out when I started doing this work, and most don't want to hear about the cases I'm working on. In the early years, my partner was very concerned that I would be emotionally disturbed by the work. He also feared that I would be exposed to and potentially harmed by the perpetrators of these crimes. He had visions of me being targeted by associates of suspects. I must admit it is a possibility, but I suspect I'm more likely to die from eating a dodgy mushroom (I'm a keen forager).

Despite our collective creeping anxieties, most of us are not likely to come to harm. Europe has one of the lower homicide rates: approximately 3 people in every 100,000 are intentionally killed every year. In comparison, in Africa and the Americas the rate is 12.5 and 16.5. Within Europe, the homicide rate in the UK is on the lower side; in 2016 there were 571 homicides (about 0.9 per 100,000). Even though in recent years there has been an increase in violent crime in this country, the overall levels are low compared to the turn of the millennium. In 2001–2 there were 891 homicides here (about 1.5 per 100,000).

Not surprisingly, the causes of this decline and recent upturn are vigorously debated, both in academia and by the press and politicians. I am reciting these rough figures partially to emphasise that we really do live in a very safe society but also to introduce a rather odd aspect of my work. Most people tend to plan their annual holidays around school holidays and bank holidays or their inability to tolerate their boss's behaviour for much longer. I tend to plan my holidays to avoid my peak season of work which is usually October to March. As far as I am aware, there is no significant increase in violent crime during those months. Burglaries are famously more frequent during the mid-winter festive season. But I have not been able to track down any evidence to suggest that homicides are more common after an omission of Brussels sprouts from the festive table. So, why am I busier at that time of year?

It appears that the absence of leaves on the trees may be to blame for my having to work outdoors in the wettest and coldest months of the year. Basically, people notice the deceased more easily when the branches are bare. We are visual animals and whilst our sense of smell is fairly good, it is deeply inferior to that of many other animals. One group of people who often report finding human remains are dog walkers as they are often alerted to the presence of the deceased by their pet. Owing to their superior sense of smell, dogs detect the dead far more easily than humans and they tend to investigate the source, especially if they are off the lead. When trees and shrubs are in full leaf and a dog bounds into the bushes, the owner is far less likely to be able to see what has aroused the excitement of their hound. As the leaves fall, our eyes take over from where our noses fail us, and the dead are revealed. I don't have any evidence to prop up this assumption, but it makes sense and I have no other reasonable explanation for why I get called to more deposition scenes at that time of the year than any other.

I don't remember how I fell in love with plants. In all probability, I didn't – I was simply born this way. My mother tells me that as far back as she can remember I reacted to their presence. I was an early June baby, and in the summer of 1968 when I was still largely immobile, mum would put me and my pram in the garden under a presciently weeping ash tree. I would stay there for hours, contentedly staring at the branches and the sky. Perhaps this is why the impending loss of up to 95 per cent of our ash trees, due to the accidental introduction of an invasive fungus, fills me with a particular pain.

Once I began to crawl, mum said that I remained most biddable. All she needed to do was place me on my grandmother's lawn in front of her flower bed full of lupins, delphiniums, irises and roses, and I would, again, sit and stare. Perhaps she should have been worried. I don't remember the day, when I was about 3 years old, I caused our lovely neighbour Elsie great distress by finding a pair of scissors and a basket and proceeded to cut every one of her rose flowers off. To make things worse, I endeavoured to cut off the unopened buds, just below the head and with no stalk. I then laid the doomed blooms neatly in the basket, knocked on her door and awaited her pleasure. Mum tells me that Elsie demonstrated great fortitude, calmly received the basket, took me round to her now monochrome-green flowerbed and explained to me how to cut roses properly, and that it needed to be in the company of an adult. No doubt afterwards she went indoors and swore quite a bit to her husband Denis. She obviously forgave me, as one of my earlier childhood memories was picking the garden peas Denis had grown and shelling them with Elsie on her back doorstep. Most of them went in my mouth.

The first plant that I truly remember was a single hyacinth bulb lying on the steps outside my childhood home. Decades later, I can still point to the exact spot. I recall being enchanted by the pearlescent, papery reddish-purple tones of its skin. Instinctively, I picked it up and turned towards my mother's rose bed, which was immediately opposite the location of my earlier rosaceous crime. I dug a shallow depression in the soil with my hands, placed the bulb into the depression, narrow end upwards, and covered the lower portion of the bulb with soil and firmed it down. I was enraptured. I stared at it and waited for something to happen. No one told me how to do this. Somehow, I just knew. The planting of the bulb was my own precious and private piece of joy. Over the next few weeks I quietly watched it start to grow, and the smooth, rich green of the emerging leaves captivated me. I became anxious and impatient when at last I saw the first signs of the flower buds being revealed from within their nest of green. One morning I ran out of the house to see if I was going to be treated to a full bloom, but I was met with a void. The bulb was gone, all that remained was a shallow depression. I was torn up with anguish and needed to discover what had happened. On interrogation, my mother confessed. She had weeded the flower bed and, not realising the bulb's significance, she had dug it up and thrown it away. I was enraged, distressed and full of loss. Mum, in her guilt, sought to make amends by offering me a strip of ground under the front wall of the house. I accepted. I now had my first garden, in which I would grow lavender, radishes and marigolds.

I'm not simply trying to charm you with tales of my childhood. My longstanding passion for plants hopefully means that I have absorbed a lot of information that is, at times, useful. For many of us, we simply don't associate plants and flowers, which bring most of us joy, with the darker side of humanity. We struggle to link the two, and I believe a major reason is that most of us simply don't notice plants, despite their being ever-present in our lives. Usually they are the first aspect of the natural world that we see each morning as we open our curtains. Plant blindness, as it's been labelled, is probably due to several factors. First, their movements are not like ours – they don't leap, walk, fly or swim in a manner that is comparable to animals. They do move, and sometimes very fast, but we just don't notice it.

We are animals with complex communication skills. Sadly, we tend to underestimate the communication and cognitive abilities of other organisms, especially plants. They can and very frequently do communicate. Our own biases have meant that it is only relatively recently that scientists have started seriously studying plant communication. Our own reliance on visual communication means that the less other organisms look like us, the less we connect with them. Thus, plants tend to be placed low in the psychological environment of most people. Our plant blindness may have deep evolutionary roots; prior to our ancestral societies developing agriculture and sedentary lifestyles, we had one eye out for the larger predators and another on the smaller ones we fancied for supper. Yes, plants were part of our lives, but we did not focus on them. A small hint of this can be seen in European, North African and Middle Eastern Palaeolithic and early Neolithic art. The period is characterised by a diverse range of cave painting, pottery and carving depicting humanity and animals that are both artistic and unambiguous. As yet, I've found only one representation that is clearly botanical. This appears to be true of most societies, with the notable exception of the aboriginal cultures of Australia: their unique depiction of plant life stretches back at least 40,000 years.

My diversion into prehistory was aimed at illustrating that humanity is predisposed to plant-blindness. This has the consequence of obscuring their value and potential. We learn at school that plants generate oxygen and without that we'd die. We may also learn that humanity is dependent for its survival on about 20 types of crop. A child may also be obliged to identify the parts of a flower and then move on to something that is allegedly more interesting. For most of us, plants only remain in our lives as the recommended five a day in our diet and an etiolated yucca behind the television. Some of us are lucky and have been drawn into the world of plants by amateur gardening or natural history. Society risks so much by overlooking plants. Their value goes so much further than what we put on our plate. For example, numerous studies have shown that being able to see plants improves recovery times in hospitals, and access to the outdoors and exercising in it can be important in improving mental health. As science continues to explore the natural world we are learning far more about how plants – and other overlooked organisms like invertebrates, fungi and bacteria – enrich our lives, providing us with the tools to tackle the challenges we face.

Curiously, forensic science isn't a science, it's the application of scientific knowledge in the pursuit of understanding how a crime took place. As such, it is a synthesis of information and skills from a very wide range of sources. Potentially, almost everything that comes into contact with humanity could be used forensically. Two factors limit the use of forensics. First, our lack of knowledge. If we are unable to understand something (for example how it works or what it's made of) then we are unable to define its potential relevance in a crime scene. People quite often question the need for primary or 'blue skies' research; to many it seems irrelevant – too abstract to be of use in the modern world. However, we often make major scientific (and economic) progress because of apparently esoteric research. Since the early 1980s, various scientists have studied and later developed techniques to produce nanostructured graphene (a form of carbon that exists in sheets of interconnected atoms). These research programmes are now starting to revolutionise many aspects of our lives such as medicine, electronics, energy storage and pollution management. When Gregor Mendel conducted his experiments on the inheritance of traits in peas *(Lathyrus oleraceus)* he was entirely unaware of the impact his work would have; it revitalised evolutionary theory and started the science of genetics and the study of DNA.

Much of the science that is used in forensics originated from a scientist thinking 'how?' or 'what?'. To foreclose on blue-skies research is to shut down future achievements that may improve all aspects of human life, including forensics. Humans have been making synthetic plastics since 1907, when Leo Baekeland invented Bakelite. Since then we have modified plastics to our needs. Many have become important in the production of clothing or other materials that require a fibrous structure. Man-made fibres may also be useful in criminal investigation. But, without prior detailed and often unrelated research, our understanding of the diversity, structure, durability and persistence of man-made fibres would be limited. For forensics to thrive, it needs to be able to source knowledge gained from the non-forensic scientific world.

Which leads to my second factor. Without adequate financial resources to research novel scientific techniques, trial their applicability and prepare them for our criminal justice system, new and potentially powerful forensic tools will not be developed. Without support for scientific innovation and the development of forensic science we risk the hamstringing of our justice system. In the Netherlands, a nationally funded body, the Netherlands Forensic Institute, conducts research on a wide range of scientific disciplines such as 'big data' and cyber-forensics, medical forensics and novel approaches to crime-scene investigation. There is no equivalent institution in the United Kingdom although several universities have their own research programmes that are supported by government funds. Additionally, police forces need to have the staff, capacity and skills to use these innovative approaches to forensic science.

People often want to know 'how easy is it to become a forensic botanist'? As far as I know, there is nowhere in the world that offers a qualification in forensic botany. To be viewed as a competent forensic botanist it would be necessary to have at least an undergraduate-level qualification in botany or plant sciences. Sadly, in the United Kingdom it is getting harder and harder to find universities that offer these courses. As well as having the basic qualifications there is a real need to have a lot of experience of field botany, which is traipsing around looking at plants in the wild.

My knowledge of plants is based upon a lifetime of observing them and the skills I learnt at university and at the Natural History Museum. This knowledge had to be reworked and applied anew when I became a forensic botanist. In general, I have never thought of myself as super clever and still don't, I simply feel I am quite bright. The oft-quoted and rather controversial maxim that 10,000 hours of practice is needed to become an expert may have a grain of truth to it. To be able to flow through diverse information environments relating to your subject and the task at hand, it is undoubtedly necessary to put the hours in. I've been looking at and studying plants for about forty-five years; lurking in my brain there is a lot of information on our plant life.

In the joyous bubble of my pre-puberty childhood, I was largely unaware that other people were not also plant mad. I also had very loyal friends. On my seventh birthday my friend Christopher endured a trip to Oxford Botanic Garden as my guest. My childhood idyll didn't last. My time at secondary school was awful and I went from being a happy child to a miserable one. I plunged from the top set ever downwards. By the time I left school, I had the second worst truancy record in the school; one of my close friends bested me. When we were about 13, we were told we needed to make plans for our future and that we'd get some assessment as to what sort of job suited us. Apparently, I was to become an insurance salesman. My school was unable to accommodate my curious interest in plants. I even volunteered to teach myself O level Latin and botany, but they were not interested. Little did they know (or care) that I'd been reading degree-level textbooks on botany since I was 10.

One year I went on a school geography field trip. I was over the moon, mainly because I really fancied the geography teacher – he had great legs and lovely hazel eyes. One day while we were walking in the uplands above Dovedale, I spotted a twayblade (*Neottia ovata*). The English name twayblade refers to its paired green leaves. It is a lovely demure orchid with small green flowers that look rather like little green aliens. The geography teacher asked me what I was looking at. I explained it was an exciting, lovely orchid and he dutifully responded with enthusiasm and asked me when it was going to flower. I told him it already was. He peered forward looking puzzled, then pitying and stood up and walked away. I blew that one! Thankfully, I had the joy of the diminutive Martian-emulating flowers of the twayblade to beguile me. They still do: the presence of their glossy paired leaves always signal to me that a botanical bounty awaits. Orchids are marvellous and complex plants. One of their peculiarities is that they have a very odd pollen. In most orchids it is aggregated into clumped structures known as pollinia and is quite unlike the dust-like pollen of other plants. Most orchids have very close ecological bonds with the insects that pollinate them. In many cases, without a suitable insect the orchid's flowers will not be pollinated, and no seed will be produced. Because of this association and the pollinia, orchid pollen is very rarely found anywhere but on the plant or on the insect. It is unlikely to be found on a suspect or at a crime scene. Pollen often appears as part of the story in many crime-scene dramas, and I'll return to this topic later.

One of the main challenges in applying my botanical knowledge to forensics is adapting my observational skills. I now look at plants in a manner I previously would not have conceived of. Generally, we botanists are used to looking at the whole plant. Or, if it is a portion of a plant, such as a flowering branch of a tree or a seed, it is normally relatively pristine. This is freqeuntly not the case in the world of forensics, as evidence gathered at a crime scene is often very fragmentary and far from ideal for identification purposes. Commonly, the object I am examining is encrusted with mud and has been trodden into the sole of a shoe or onto a car wheel arch. Sometimes, the plant material is heavily degraded owing to protracted contact with decaying human tissue or has been exposed to the elements for long periods. I have had to draw upon the vast swathes of fully or partially recalled botanical experiences embedded within my memory to help me pull an identification to the surface of my mind.

My early childhood was spent exploring the plants and the countryside around my Warwickshire home and my grandparents' house in Cornwall. These adventures helped foster an understanding of how landscapes in this country have evolved over time and have the form they do today. I remember collecting blackberries with my mother in some low-lying fields when I was a small boy and noticing the curious undulations in the land. I later came to learn that they were ridge and furrow, the remains of Saxon agriculture. Not only do they undulate appealingly but the gentle gradient creates niches in which a variety of wild plants can thrive. Sadly, most of the ones in our village were destroyed, first by ploughing for arable crops, and then by the arrival of the M40. The regular up and downward curves of these mounds create subtly varying growing conditions for plants. An experienced botanical eye will notice that at the bottom of the slope, where it is wetter, creeping buttercup (*Ranunculus repens*) grows; as the soil becomes somewhat dryer, meadow buttercup (*R. acris*) prevails; and, perched on and near the summit where the soil is driest, grows bulbous buttercup (*R. bulbosus*), the rounded bulbous rootstock providing it with stored water and nutrients for the hot summer months.

A childhood spent observing the ways of wild plants and cultivating plants in gardens helped fashion my observational skills. I still recall my fascination with reading scientific plant names as a child – they seemed to convey something magical. By the time I was seven I was reading gardening and wildflower books and absorbing the names. Like many people I have met later in life, I was enthralled by the lovely artwork of Rev. William Keeble Martin's *New Concise British Flora*, and I scoured the pages for new words and facts. The image of marsh sow-thistle (*Sonchus palustris*), a rare plant of fens and marshes of South-East England, particularly captured my imagination. It was almost thirty-five years before I saw it in the wild, and my fascination and love was renewed.

4
Brambles and Buddleja

Many of us enjoy a walk through a wood in autumn. We take pleasure in the weakening rays of the sun and the autumnal scent of freshly fallen leaves. Whilst gazing at the hazy beauty of a fog-laden wood, all too often we trip up. Our feet have been snagged by a bramble stem. After some cursing and attempting to remove the offending briar from the path, we return home. For many of us, that is as far as our relationship with brambles goes. Some of us may enjoy blackberry picking and eating blackberry and apple pie or blackberry jam, but that is all. It's an oddity of the English language that when we don't like them, we call them 'brambles' and when they give us pleasure, they are 'blackberries'.

I am rather fond of brambles, though not as fond of them as batologists, to whom I shall return shortly. Why the fondness? First, being a botanist, I'm keen on all plants and I cannot think of a wild plant that I am unable to admire, although, it is fair to say that some more heavily hybridised varieties of garden plant leave me a little cold. Back to brambles: their role in the ecology of our countryside is probably one of the more important of our wild plants. When in flower, they provide nectar and pollen for a myriad of invertebrates. Their roots, stems and foliage are food for many more, as well as for various mammals such as deer. Wild boars are like them, too; the young shoots and roots are a tasty snack, and the boars' penetrating snouts churn up the soil and create new habitat for other wildlife.

Brambles even host a range of specialist fungi that call them home. I'm particularly fond of fungi. To date, I've not had an opportunity to work with them in a crime scene. I have had to content myself with looking at fungal fruiting bodies at a crime scene and contemplating how they may be of use. Being inquisitive is a double-edged sword though, as it is very easy to divert your mental energy to interesting but ultimately unproductive avenues of thought and examination. I'm usually brought to the present by Sophie calling me to order by muttering 'eyes on the job Spencer'. One day I'll show her! However, being curious can be very productive, because it often enables you to look at a case in a way that the police team had not conceived of. This is particularly true of botany – most investigators have never worked a case that has a botanical angle. One of the more common and easily seen fungi to grow on brambles is the violet bramble rust (*Phragmidium violaceum*). Violet bramble rust is an obligate biotroph, which means that it is unable to complete its rather complex life history without the presence of brambles. It can be seen as reddish-purple blotches on bramble leaves through summer until the leaves fall in autumn. Of course, we most value brambles for their fruit, as do some wildlife. The fruit of these plants are an invaluable food source for many species in late summer.

However, the main reason I am fond of brambles is because I often encounter them at crime scenes. I am happy to see them not only because I value them for their aesthetic or ecological value but because they are often of assistance to me in my role as a forensic botanist. Some types of brambles are common in places where people abound and where crimes are committed. This is not because they have an affinity for humanity but because humans tend to increase the nutrient load of soil and water courses (mainly through agriculture, sewage and transport). Brambles thrive in these conditions; they are greedy feeders and the extra nutrients we supply are to their liking.

So, why are brambles of use when investigating crime scenes? Brambles can be thought of as vegetable calendars (all plants are for that matter; we just need to learn how to understand them). They can be of assistance in estimating how long a person's remains have been at the location they're in. Quite often when a body is first found, the police will not know who the person is. To establish their identity, the police will pursue various avenues of investigation. One important question will be 'how long has this person been here?'. In some cases, brambles (and other plants too) may help resolve that question. Despite appearing chaotic and messy to us, a bramble thicket is not disordered. It is an elegant and choreographed structure that enables the bramble plant to maximise its potential within its environment.

To understand how brambles grow it helps to know and understand the other plants they are related to. Brambles are members of the rose family (*Rosaceae*). The rose family is a fairly large one, with nearly 3,000 species (for comparison, there are about 28,000 types of wild orchid). Members of the family include, not surprisingly, the rose (*Rosa*) as well as plums and cherries (*Prunus*), apples (*Malus*), hawthorns (*Crataegus*) and strawberries (*Fragaria*). Of these, brambles are most like strawberries. Both plants have similarities in fruit structure, but more importantly, aspects of their growth are also comparable. Strawberry plants have a short, stout rootstock that produce long, thin trailing stems (runners) from which new plants develop.

Brambles, and their close relative raspberry (*Rubus idaeus*), have a variation on this body plan. Every spring, the plant sends up one or more fresh vegetative growths (these are called canes in gardening), whose role is to increase the physical territory that the plant occupies and outcompete other plants. With brambles, the growing tips of these stem arch, and when the tips meet the ground, they produce fresh roots and a new plant. This is why brambles are so good at tripping us up; they're often rooted at both ends – creating a natural tripwire. The following year the same stem changes its function; it produces shorter side-shoots, which flower and then bear fruit. During the summer, when the plant is flowering, further vegetative shoots arise from the ground and grow through and over the flowering stems. Over a period of years, the plant steadily gets larger as the fresh stems overtop the older ones (which gradually weaken and die).

Thus, for all their chaotic demeanour to us, brambles are very 'organised' plants with an effective strategy for surviving in our hedgerows, woodlands and the nutrient-rich corners of our habitations, where many crimes are committed.

The ability of brambles to gradually encapsulate territory is of value to me as a forensic botanist. Once a deceased person is in the environment, plants and animals respond to and accommodate their presence. If a person's remains become surrounded by bramble plants, they will soon be covered by the plants' enshrouding growth, awaiting discovery. It is my role to use the tell-tale signs in the plant's structure to estimate how long the person has been where they are. This involves carefully examining the position of the stems arising from the root stock, as well as observing how the stems have aged. I will examine as many rootstocks as possible on which to base my conclusions and I may need to take samples for more detailed examination afterwards.

I have revealed how brambles can help fight crime. But what of batology? Brambles, alongside some other members of the rose family, such as the whitebeams (*Sorbus*), have a rather curious way of reproducing. They don't have sex. Or, to be more accurate, most of them don't have sex. Many bramble species reproduce by apomixis (a rather handy Scrabble word), which results in the formation of a seed without the necessity for fertilisation. Apomixis is a complex phenomenon that is fairly widespread in flowering plants. One of its consequences is that these asexual brambles are effectively vegetative clones; another is that they are often very restricted in their range and extremely rare. The Trelleck bramble (*Rubus trelleckensis*) is restricted to Beacon Hill in Monmouthshire, Wales, and may be vulnerable to extinction. It is not alone in this regard. Many of the 300 or more recognised micro-species of *Rubus fruticosus* agg. (the collective term for this group of brambles) found in Britain and Ireland are similarly scarce. They are known as micro-species because the characteristics used to separate them are often very subtle, often microscopic. The complexity and diversity of brambles is such that relatively few botanists among us are brave enough to embrace them. Those who do are known as batologists, a name derived from the ancient Greek (báton) for blackberry. Becoming a batologist takes time, patience and iron-clad fingertips. During my time at the Natural History Museum in London I had the honour of becoming acquainted with the king of British and Irish batology, David Ellis Allen. Not only is he a man of vast knowledge on brambles but his erudition in natural history and the history of our nation's botany collections is remarkable.

At this point, I am hoping you may feel a warm glow when thinking of these plants. Sadly, all is not rosy with brambles. All too often, ecological damage is one of the consequences of humanity's activities on this planet. In many cases, this damage is caused by invasive non-native species. Owing to their tasty fruit, we have taken our brambles from their homelands and transported them all over the world. For many places, such as New Zealand and Hawaii, the consequences have been disastrous. Many of Hawaii's incredibly endangered plants are under threat due to competition with invasive non-native brambles and the damage caused by the feral pigs that forage on them. Luckily, in some cases control measures have been found. The violet bramble rust fungus has been introduced to areas such as New Zealand, where it is used as a biocontrol agent against invasive brambles. The fungus is so specialised and specific in its requirements that it is considered extremely unlikely that it will move to an alternative host.

The humble bramble is so much more than an annoying tripwire. Embrace its wonder next time you stumble over one in your local wood or park.

I moved to London in 1989. Back then, the streets of Hackney where I lived, were not full of elegant hipsters. There was a lot of rubbish, though. Before London, I had lived near Diss in Norfolk, where I'd worked for the prestigious Blooms of Bressingham, at the time one of the most important horticultural nurseries in the country. While I was there, I successfully applied for a studentship at the Royal Botanic Gardens, Kew. My last summer in Diss was chiefly spent in a large, rambling farmhouse, all crooked stairs and dark passageways, with an equally rambling household. I lived in one portion of the house with young horticulture students who also worked for Blooms, and the family who owned the property lived in another portion. The house had a delightful and weed-filled walled garden with a fine veteran mulberry tree. My friends and I spent many summer evenings sitting under that tree, enjoying a drink. It was a lovely place, although at times I was slightly irked by being woken up at seven in the morning by the guitar-playing evangelical Christians who had possession of the remaining portion of the building.

One of the people living in the house was called Simon. He was an intense young man who lived in the evangelical wing of the house. He had travelled far and wide and had spent some time in Africa working on an experimental agricultural research station. He'd brought some seed back from his time there, and he shared some of the seed with me. One of the plants that I grew from his present was white leadtree or jumbay (*Leucaena leucocephala*). In the 1970s and early 1980s, this Mexican plant was considered a miracle tree that would help reduce rural poverty in arid tropical regions of the world. As a consequence it was introduced to new regions worldwide. It is drought resistant, produces firewood and is excellent fodder for animals. Since then, its reputation has descended from these exalted heights and it is now considered one of the more serious invasive non-native trees globally. It is also remarkably hardy. One of my plants has survived in a sheltered corner outdoors in central London for the last decade, and it has successfully produced a second generation.

My jumbay plant reminds me of my times in Norfolk and of Simon. It also reminds me of a terrible turn of events. A few months after I arrived in London, he moved down as well. At the time, squatting was legal and I ended up in a large community of squats in Hackney. About two hundred of us lived on two streets near London Fields. Simon chose to live in a house that was barely standing. Being remarkably talented, he rebuilt the house himself. Without his efforts, the house would no doubt have been condemned and fallen down years ago. Now, it overlooks London Fields and the hordes of sunbathing new urbanites of Hackney.

I always found Simon a little too intense and charged for my liking, and I tended to keep contact with him to a minimum. I would occasionally visit him for a chat and a cup of tea and obligingly admire his latest piece of renovation. One day, as I was walking to the park on my way into Soho, Simon invited me in. He led me into the basement of the house and started extolling his latest building achievements. He invited me to sit down in the sole chair in the room. As I did so, he became particularly animated about the concrete flooring he'd just completed. Simon really wanted me to approve of the wonderful finish and the quality of the work. I mumbled some appreciative sentences and made my escape. A few months later, Simon moved out of the country and I never saw him again.

I did hear about him, though. A couple of years later, I learnt that Simon had just been charged with murder or manslaughter. In the intervening time, he'd travelled around the world once more, but by degrees his conscience weighed upon him and he'd returned to this country. He walked into a police station and confessed to killing a man. While he had been renovating the house, he had befriended a younger man who was homeless, and he invited him to share the house. For some unknown reason, one evening Simon killed the other man with either an axe or a heavy spade. He then buried the man in the basement and concreted the floor over. The very floor he'd been so keen for me to approve of. I'd been standing on top of his victim. To this day, I don't know the details of the police investigation, but as Simon made a full confession, they are unlikely to have needed to use clues from the natural world to establish when he died. The awful postscript to this story is that the identity of the young man he killed is unknown. Somewhere, someone is wondering what happened to him.

One plant that always reminds me of Hackney and the almost forgotten murder of the unknown young man, is buddleia. Its omnipresence in urban and suburban Britain leads many to believe that it is a native wild plant. It's not: the first time it was recorded in the wild here was in the 1920s. Since then it has gone on to occupy thousands of hectares of land. In the south-east it is certainly far more abundant than Japanese knotweed and probably causes far more environmental damage. I first started to notice the abundance of buddleia after I became a student at Kew Gardens. My train commute from Hackney to Kew gave me the opportunity to watch this plant colonise London's railways and wastelands (botanically speaking, they are anything but 'waste'; they are floral havens, full of fascinating native and non-native plants). My time at Kew was a mixed experience. I learned a huge amount and I encountered fantastic people and amazing plants. But, like a lot of others, growing up gay in the 1980s had left its scars. Being told by the national media and public opinion, almost daily, that 'your kind' are all evil paedophiles and that you'll rot in hell after dying of AIDS is no joke. Quietly, I unravelled. I ran away from my life and hid. Staff at Kew tried to get me to return but I could not bear the thought. I finally realised that working in horticulture wasn't for me. I then spent several years misbehaving and working in bars. Later on, I worked in a further education college as a Personnel Officer, in the days before the profession mutated into Human Resources.

During this time, I was quite disconnected from the world of plants. Except for the ones in my garden and on the windowsill, including a cactus I'd had since I was seven; I still have it over 40 years later. Growing up in the country, I was used to fields of flowers (sadly now largely gone), and the idea that the wild plants in the urban environment could be truly interesting eluded me. I later came to appreciate the 'weeds' of our cities and this in turn has helped me look on familiar plants, such as the bramble, in a new light.

Brambles and *Buddleja* vie for space in our urban and suburban landscapes. They often share that space with the homeless. The steady escalation in numbers of the homeless on our streets should be cause for national shame. Not only is each one a personal tragedy but the burden for their care is being thrust upon the police and other emergency services. Each year as we move deeper into winter, the number of people dying outside in our towns and cities climbs upwards. Most of those people are found within hours. But on occasion, those who sought safety and shelter in the urban wastelands and woods are left alone for weeks, months or even years. Railway sidings and embankments are particularly favoured spots.

I was once called to a potential crime scene where the heavily decayed remains of a man had been found. It was the middle of winter and, as usual, bitterly cold. Heavy rain had been falling for several days and the ground was very wet and slippery. I said hello to the officer managing the perimeter and signed myself in. There was a press photographer with a cumbersome camera in the middle distance trying to assess where they could best get some decent shots. Sploshing through the soggy football pitch by the railway embankment I approached the CSM and introduced myself. The railway embankment was steep, and we all had to resist slithering back down as we hauled ourselves up to where the man lay. He was wearing all-weather gear and was lying, straight legged, on his back facing the sky. The wonderous work of the microbial community had progressed a long way; there was relatively little flesh remaining on his face. His lower jaw was slightly dropped and most of his teeth could be seen. As I leant in, I tried not to stumble, the soil sliding from underneath me. There was a fairly strong smell of decay, but the low temperature meant that the volatile organic compounds that cause the decay smell were less mobile in the air. If it had been hot, the smell from the man's remains would have been almost overpowering.

We decided to retreat down the slope and discuss how we were going to document the scene and get the man's remains down the slope safely, all while remaining physically intact ourselves. The PolSA team had to build a common entry path using ladders laid on the surface of the slope, and, while they were doing that, I tried not to fret too much about the damage they were doing to the vegetation. It is quite hard to persuade half a dozen large, wet PolSAs not to damage the bushes as they scramble up a railway embankment in the pouring rain. So, I decided to back off and go for a quick tea break.

Once the ladders were in place, we headed back up. As the forensic anthropologist worked on making an assessment of the man, I started to look at the vegetation around and underneath him. I looked out towards the surrounding houses, roads and the football pitch. These were the last things he saw. His body appeared quite composed, his legs stretched out below him facing down the slope and his arms by his side. The vegetation surrounding him showed no signs of significant damage, apart from that caused by our team and the person who discovered him. As is so often the case, it was a dog walker. The lack of damage to the vegetation appeared to rule out a struggle or a fight, and I couldn't see signs of an exit route created by another person through the nettles, brambles, buddleia and Japanese knotweed. The upper torso, head and arms of the man were resting on the remains of the vegetation flattened by the weight of his body. His lower torso and legs appeared to have slid underneath the sprawling stems of a bramble bush. It was rather like he'd climbed into bed and pulled up the blanket halfway.

Overall, the vegetation evidence suggested that he simply stopped walking, lay down and died. It seemed almost peaceful. I made my notes of the scene, and while the forensic anthropologist and the PolSA team worked to carefully lift his remains and get them down the slope, I set myself the task of finding his route to his final resting place. I had to move very carefully through the vegetation; I didn't want to slip and disturb anything. After about half an hour, I started to feel that I could trace his last steps. The damage to plant stems and branches, most of which were Japanese knotweed, was erratic. He appeared to have veered up and down the bank for about thirty metres. I can't be certain, for I was not there when he died, but within the vegetation were traces of a man's last movement, lurching about, alone in the undergrowth until he came to a stop and died.

The knotweed provided very useful information on when the man died as well as the route he took. Japanese knotweed is infamous, particularly now that its invasiveness has had an impact upon the saleability of properties. It's also a remarkable plant. Nearly all the Japanese knotweed in Britain and Ireland is from a single clone, a female. This is also true of the majority of the Japanese knotweed plants that escaped cultivation around the world: they are derived from the same clone. As Japanese knotweed is a widespread invasive non-native species in many parts of the world,especially Europe and North America, the plant is the largest and most successful female on the planet. It surprises people that the three-metre-high stems are each less than a year old. Every spring, the stems grow from the perennial underground rootstock. Yet despite being vigorous and all-conquering, individual Japanese knotweed stems are quite easy to damage and the effects can be seen for months after. As I examined the knotweed at the scene, I could see that the damaged portions included the smaller side branches supporting the fluffy white flowers. These flowers open late summer and, because the stems were damaged during the flowering season, I was able to provide an estimate of how long the man's remains had been there. Several months.

A few days later I learnt that the man had been identified. He had been physically and mentally unwell for several years and had not been seen by family members for at least a year. I was also told that there was information to suggest that he'd been sleeping rough and that the post-mortem was unable to identify a cause of death. He was too badly decayed. Tragically, a vulnerable person fell through the net and, quite literally, the police had to pick up the pieces.

5

Tales of Knives and Wood

Despite the widespread cachet, forensics is not glamorous. Frost- and filth-encrusted ditches by trunk roads have limited appeal. And the work rarely achieves the suspenseful scenarios enacted in television crime dramas. Usually, the work is slow and laborious; however on occasion, it becomes charged with suspense. Sometimes, as it progresses and the secrets of a scene are revealed, the atmosphere increasingly takes on a dramatic air.

This atmosphere of unfolding drama once developed at a suspected crime scene I was called to, where human remains had been discovered. Somebody had found them while walking their dog along their usual daily route. The owner followed their dog off the path and found themselves in a small clearing walled in with a dense growth of vegetation, and in the middle was the burnt-out remains of a large fire. The dog walker noticed some bones projecting from the ashes and retreated to call the police. Having received the call requesting I attend the scene, I rushed out of the herbarium at the Natural History Museum, headed home and stuffed a few clothes and toiletries in a bag – it might have been an overnight stay. I then hurtled towards Euston station to catch my train.

On the train, a Virgin Pendolino – my least favourite train, horrible, cramped, stinky things – I gazed out of the window and gloomily watched the lurid, pesticide and fertiliser-drenched landscape of south-east England pass by. This country of ours may appear to be a green and pleasant land, but much of it is dying and we are to blame. Aside from cursing our idiocy, I mentally evaded the pong of the Pendolino by musing about potential grave or deposition scenes. I found myself looking at small patches of scrubland on the outskirts of market towns or neglected and disused railway embankments running through the gutted former industrial heartlands wondering what secrets they held. Clearly this was idle musing, but no doubt some of those places do harbour the remains of the lost and missed. There are two or three stretches of our mainlines where I can see railway embankments or shady streamsides where, in the past, I have worked with the remains of the dead. Every time I pass these locations, I quietly say hello to the deceased.

Having rushed from Euston I was very relieved to find that the scene had remained largely undisturbed since its discovery. This is not always the case. All too often I arrive at a scene to find it has been razed to the ground by the PolSA team. It's quite hard to assess vegetation when it is piled ten foot high. The scene was in a small area of a former industrial site surrounded by modern housing. Through it ran the remains of the disused railway siding that had serviced the industry. The track bed of the railway was now a footpath. On one side it sloped down to a verge and the road where the police vehicles were parked. On the other, it was hemmed in by a profusion of planted hedging and wild plants that had colonised the area. Beneath a young ash tree by the path edge, a small track led down the embankment into the clearing. Having donned my protective wear, I clambered down the short but steep slope to the level ground below.

The clearing was about five metres across and surrounded by tall scrub and small trees, with vigorous beds of near dormant nettles and brambles beneath. It was early spring and most of the vegetation had not fully burst into regrowth. Looking upwards, I was surrounded by an arena of foliage, with no sign of the nearby houses. Not surprisingly, the clearing appeared to have been used by the homeless, as they probably felt safe here. There were signs of past habitation: old clothes, empty beer cans and cheap spirt bottles mixed in with the remains of food packaging. Around the margins of the clearing there were piles of domestic rubble and wood, which appeared to have been fly-tipped by the slothful and the selfish.

Near the middle of the clearing, a large mound of wood-ash and partially burnt timber was surrounded by several people. One was Sophie's boss, Helen, whom I'd not worked with before, but we'd spoken on the phone. With her was Toby, an expert in among other things, fire damage. There was also a CSM and a pathologist. I moved forward and joined the huddle.

The dense surrounding vegetation provided shelter, but it was still rather nippy, about five degrees celsius. The chilly-white first blooms of that spring herald, blackthorn *(Prunus spinosa)*, were just opening. I was glad of my thermals as well as the protective gear. As we looked down, I could see several strands of bramble tracking across parts of the fire pit; they were partially burnt but were also showing some signs of regrowth. Helen explained that it was not known for certain how long the remains had been there or to whom they belonged. The police had already been knocking on nearby doors asking if anyone had seen anything suspicious. Several householders said that they'd noticed smoke above the area a few weeks earlier. This was not unusual as the area was known for the accumulation of teenagers, as well as the homeless.

The information about the smoke was considered important, and the police had already started to focus their intelligence-gathering efforts around that date. They were keen to know if our assessment of the site supported the idea that the person's remains had been there for a relatively short time. After discussion about how to proceed, we each set to our task. I was particularly interested in the burn patterns on the bramble stems arching around and over the burn site. There were also signs of past scorching on the stems of the nearby shrubs. Both the brambles and the bushes had since regrown, and I was starting to get the impression that there had been multiple fires at the site and that the recent one was probably rather small compared to the earlier ones.

Mindful that I was potentially encroaching onto another person's area of expertise, I asked Toby to take a look at my observations and seek his advice. After all, he knew fires and I know plants. Thankfully, Toby was satisfied that my observations were sound.

While we all have our specialisms, it is always good to have someone else to discuss ideas and observations with. It is all too easy to allow ideas with unconscious biases to run away with themselves. I returned to the bramble stems and redoubled my efforts to absorb the patterns of the fire damage once more. The fire that damaged these stems hadn't occurred recently; the main shoots bore scorch marks along their length but the side branches coming out from them were free of damage. The plant must have regrown for several weeks after the fire. As I knelt shivering, looking at the blackthorn, it was clear that the growth must have occurred during the previous growing season which was the previous summer and early autumn. The main fire occurred at least six months ago. The police might have to change their intelligence-gathering strategy.

After an hour or so of further note taking and photography, we walked back to the police vehicles for a quick coffee break. As usual, it was the instant, paper-cup variety. The smell of the coffee has an extra resonance for me. When I was a teenager, my school was a couple of miles away from a major instant-coffee manufacturing facility, and some days the cloying, sickly, burnt, chemicalised coffee smell was overpowering and left us reeling with headaches. Perhaps it's that, rather than my membership of the bleeding-heart metropolitan elite, that makes me shudder at the sight of instant coffee. Being a well brought-up boy, I never complain, of course.

As we warmed up, we discussed our observations and next steps. We then proceeded to start removing the debris that still shrouded the remains. This had to be done slowly and carefully, as each piece of wood, entangled bramble stem or tin can would need to be examined carefully before being placed to one side. As we gathered around the remains, Helen took the lead in removing the first pieces of wood. We all huddled around and peered into the ashy debris, trying to discern how the person's body was positioned. Each piece of wood, brick or broken breezeblock that we removed exposed more of the remains. We located the lower limbs; the fire was so intense that any clothing that might once have been worn was gone, and the smaller bones had been reduced to ash and were irretrievable.

The pathologist and Helen occasionally passed comment on aspects of the bones that I didn't fully understand, but it was clear that the fire had caused so much damage it was unlikely that a cause of death would be easily established. We moved to the upper part of the body, arms and head, which was quite tricky. The skull was very brittle owing to the heat it had been exposed to, and it was caught up within a tangle of bramble stems, wire and small pieces of wood.

Each one of us was working in close proximity, huddled up and doing our best not to disturb anything. I could feel myself starting to sweat, not from tension but because even in the cold the protective clothing we have to wear can be rather humid. Each of us shifted our weight every now and then to alleviate cramping. Finally, most of the arms and the skull were visible, and we were able to proceed with clearing the debris from the upper torso. Helen pulled back two or three sheets of plywood and moved them to one side. Beneath these was what looked like part of a door and, as this was lifted off, we all gasped in surprise.

The cause of death was no longer a mystery. Lying flat across the centre of the chest was a carving knife. We all felt a ripple of excitement and for a few minutes we were slightly agog, even Helen, who is a vastly experienced forensic anthropologist. It was clear that the deceased had met their end at the furious hand of another.

At the end of the day and after we had all recovered from our excitement at the discovery of the knife, I returned to London, report writing and my life as a museum curator. Report writing is essential but mundane and far from the thrill of a television drama or documentary. Like many other people, I have seen *Silent Witness* but only when it first started. I quite enjoyed it, but my interest soon petered out: no Christopher Meloni.

A few months later I learned that a family member was charged with the murder and subsequently found guilty. At the trial, there was no need to present the botanical evidence that helped establish how long the body had been where it was found, and I wasn't called as an expert witness. I'm confident the knife was discussed!

It may surprise you to learn that botany has also been used in the courtroom for quite some time. Plant-based evidence has been used in courts for at least 90 years. The most celebrated early case is the kidnapping and murder of the infant son of the famous pioneer aviator, Charles Lindbergh. During the evening of 1 March 1932, Charles Augustus Lindbergh Jr. was taken from his cot in an upstairs bedroom of the family home in Hopewell, New Jersey. On discovering the infant was gone the next morning, his father and the family's staff found a ransom note and searched the house and grounds. The police were then called, and a makeshift, home-made ladder was soon found lying on the ground about 30 metres from the house. A little over four years later, Richard 'Bruno' Hauptmann, a German émigré, was executed for the child's kidnap and murder.

The Lindbergh case is one of the most infamous in modern American history; it also had far-reaching consequences and is still shrouded in controversy. I'm going to sidestep the controversy and concentrate on the botany. The home-made ladder was considered to be one of the most significant pieces of evidence in the case. The scientist who examined the ladder was Dr Arthur Koehler from Madison, Wisconsin. Koehler worked for the Forest Products Laboratory which is part of the United States Forest Service. He was an expert on wood anatomy and during his testimony he described himself as 'the expert on the identification of wood for the Government.'.

Prior to the arrest of Hauptman, Koehler had examined the ladder and had identified the wood as coming from North Carolina pine *(Pinus taeda)*. Today, this pine is more commonly known as Loblolly pine. Using microscopy, he was also able to determine that the machine tooling on the surface of the wood was made by blades rotating at 2,700 revolutions per minute, cutting the wood at a rate of 258 feet per minute. To be honest, I don't have a clue how he achieved this, but it is extremely clever! Koehler then sent enquiries to over 1,500 wood mills, and this list was then whittled down to 25. Each of the 25 mills were sent a request to produce a sample of planed wood for comparison with the ladder. Of these, the sample sent back by M.G. & J.J. Dorn Company from McCormick, South Carolina proved to be the best match. Further investigation of the company's order book and shipment records lead to Koehler, identifying the National Lumber and Millwork Company in the Bronx as the retail source of the timber from the ladder.

During this phase of his investigation, Koehler also advised the investigating team to seize any woodworking tools, especially planes, that might be in the possession of any arrested suspects. Months later, when Bruno Hauptmann was arrested, a carpenter's tool kit was found in his possession and in the toolkit was a plane. It was also discovered that he'd worked for the National Lumber and Millwork Company and had purchased timber from there. Careful examination of irregularities in the blade of Hauptmann's plane by Koehler demonstrated that it had been used to plane the wood of the ladder: the cut surface of the wood had irregularities matching the blade from Hauptmann's plane. Also, a small chisel was missing from Hauptmann's carpentry set, the same size and make as a chisel found at the crime scene.

Koehler was also able to demonstrate that the treads of the ladder originated from parts of the staircase and flooring in the attic in the property in which Hauptmann lived. Crucially, a part of the ladder, exhibited in the trial as 'rail 16', matched a sawn-off floorboard in the attic of Hauptmann's home. The pattern of the annual growth rings of the wood and their curvature on rail 16 and the floorboard were an exact match. On top of this, Koehler also demonstrated that four empty square-cut nail holes found on the ladder's wood were a match for the distribution of the missing wood and nail holes found in the attic.

Shortly after the trial, Koehler was interviewed on radio and stated 'In all the years of my work, I have become convinced of the absolute reliability of the testimony of trees. They carry in themselves the record of their history. They show with absolute fidelity the progress of the years, storms, droughts, floods, injuries, and any human touch. A tree never lies. You cannot fake or make a tree.' While his proclamation may seem rather grandiose, basically he was right. I don't think anyone has yet managed to fake tree rings! However, we are all capable of misinterpreting what we see before us. One of the key requirements to be a good scientist is to ensure that your conclusions can be supported by your observations.

Another requirement is: don't rush. Rushing work to keep clients happy is never wise. To the best of my knowledge, I have only made one mistake in my work for the police. I misidentified a leaf. I foolishly attempted to identify the leaf from photographs supplied by the police. Based upon my observation, I though the leaf was of value evidentially. Photography can be a very valuable tool, but it can also be very misleading, and in this case, I allowed myself to be misled. The angle from which the photo was taken obscured some of the features necessary for correct identification. Hours later, I received an extra batch of images from the police that showed I had misidentified the leaf. As a consequence, it was not evidentially important. After a few moments of cold blood running through my veins, I picked up the phone. Although the detective was polite, I could sense the gritted teeth. Police forces quite often ask my opinion based upon photographs taken by their own team. Unfortunately, I've yet to meet a botanically inclined police officer, and they invariably take awful pictures of plants and vegetation in general. The images are either landscape scale and not focused on the vegetation, or they are somewhat abstract images of part of a leaf or a flower. It's not their fault; without proper training they won't be able to photograph the salient features of a plant or vegetation to aid identification or to get a botanical feel of a crime scene.

Although the Lindbergh case is sometimes described as the first case of botanical evidence used in serious crime, there are earlier instances. Indeed, near the start of his testimony at the Lindbergh trial, Koehler explained that he had prior experience of criminal investigations. In 1923 Koehler gave evidence at the murder trial of John Magnuson in Wisconsin. Magnuson, a farmer, was involved in a disagreement with the local authorities over plans to dig drainage ditches across his land. On top of this, they planned to tax him to pay for the work. As the dispute escalated, a dredging machine loaded with 200 gallons of gasoline and diesel blew up. Although foul play couldn't be proven, many suspected it was not an accident and blamed Magnuson. Finally, two days after Christmas, tragedy struck when a pipe bomb was sent, disguised in a parcel, to the home of James Chapman, a county commissioner and enemy of Magnuson. The bomb severely wounded Chapman and killed his wife, Clementine. Koehler testified at the trial of Magnuson, by then known as the Yule Bomber, and by using microscopic comparison was able to show that the white elm (*Ulmus americana*) wood used to house the device was the same as some of the wood shavings taken from Magnuson's work bench.

So, Koehler had previous experience of examining wood as part of a criminal investigation. Sensing that his testimony could prove damning, one of Hauptmann's defence team, Frederick Pope, attempted to prevent Koehler from proceeding. Pope objected by saying that 'this witness is not qualified to express an opinion regarding wood', which he further qualified by adding, 'We say that there is no such animal known among men as an expert on wood; that it is not a science that has been recognized by the courts; that it is not in a class with handwriting experts or with ballistic experts. But this is no science, this is merely a man who has had a lot of experience in examining trees, who knows the barks on trees and a few things like that.' Pope then proceeded to liken Koehler's knowledge to that of members of the jury – it was ordinary and of no particular merit. His attempt failed and, after some probing of Koehler's qualifications and experience, the judge, Thomas W. Trenchard, declared, 'I would say to counsel now I deem this witness to be qualified as an expert.'. Trenchard's statement is a pivotal moment, when the use of botany in criminal investigations was acknowledged to be on a comparable footing to other science-based techniques such as fingerprint analysis.

Kohler's experience of a barrister attempting to reduce his experience to that of someone who 'knows the barks on trees and a few things like that' is reflective of a deeply ingrained ambivalence to plants in our societies. It is also true that this ambivalence towards botany and environmental forensics often still plays out when I attend a crime scene.

6
The Layby

The longest and most complex case I have worked on involved the awful murder of a woman who had been savagely killed by her estranged husband. He beat her to death while their children waited for her in another part of the house. With the knowledge of family members, he then drove to a secluded spot and dumped her body.

Shortly afterwards, he was arrested and charged with her murder. Unfortunately, despite repeated interviews, the suspect was either unwilling or unable to lead the police to the woman's remains. The family members who assisted the suspect confessed to having helped him dispose of the body in a layby. They and the suspect claimed to not remember where. Initially, the police had limited information to go on regarding her whereabouts, witness statements were vague and potentially unreliable. After much painstaking work involving mobile phone signal data, automatic number-plate recognition (ANPR) and appeals to the public, the police believed that they knew on which stretch of road her remains were. Unfortunately, the area was still very large, approximately 10 miles of major road, much of it dual carriageway. After several months of searching laybys along the stretch of road, the police decided to seek the professional skills of the forensic anthropologist Sophie.

Sophie calls me to assist with the search. There are numerous laybys along the route. So far, the police have largely concentrated their efforts on two of them. They have a long way to go. Before arriving at the scene, I receive various maps from the police detailing the search areas. These arrive either on encrypted CDs or via secure email. I also have quite a long discussion on the phone with Sophie. The first site we are surveying is large and complex, with a range of ditches, ancient hedgerows, streams, woodland and pasture. This land is adjacent to a large and heavily used layby on the main road. It is going to be noisy. It is also likely that we're going to attract the attention of the press.

After a longish journey from London, I arrive early in a small town in northern England. It's fairly affluent but there still isn't a decent coffee shop around. I mutter to myself and grumble away because I've been up since about 5 and I hate mornings. It's also bloody freezing; after 30 years in London I've become soft. I used to be tough. The house I spent my early teens in during the early 1980s was so cold that one winter a glass of milk by the side of my mother's bed froze solid overnight. I brace myself for meeting Sophie; she'll be fully conscious and requiring my undivided attention, quite rightly so. Her car pulls up and I stumble forward. As we drive out of the town and get onto the bypass, Sophie runs through the case again while I strive to look intelligent. She knows me well enough by now to realise it's a sham. We also catch up on gossip: how are things in her office, how's life in the museum, what have her children got up to, that sort of thing. I enjoy Sophie's company – she's got a sense of humour and a forthrightness that is very much to my liking. Both of us would make terrible poker players because our faces generally depict quite clearly what we think of others and their decisions; especially if we think they're being dumb or bullish!

As we near the layby, I can see two police vans, a marked police car and an unmarked car. The latter will probably be the detectives'. The landscape is very flat, a typical flood plain. I can already sense what the soil will be like. I have a rough map of the geology of England in my head and based on that I'm quite good at assessing soil types from a car window. I'm also playing a small mind game with myself – predicting what plant species I'll encounter once I step out of the car. Parts of the landscape are clearly rather old, as the hedgerows look ancient even from a distance. On the other hand, the wood is very recent in origin, probably less than 30 years old. No doubt it was planted to shelter the nearby housing estates when the bypass was built. It looks like a woodland and has largish trees, but its ground flora will be very limited. To me this is not woodland, it's plantation. I force myself to fully engage my still half-numb brain. As I step out of the car, my reacquaintance with the cold helps. I also remind myself that each police force and investigating team is different. I have to learn the behaviours and foibles of each new team as I come into contact with them. Generally, this involves me keeping my mouth shut for a while. It won't last.

I soon realise that I have worked with some of the team before. Overall, I'm happy because I've worked with this force several times and rather like them. But I also know that I'm going to have to live off crisps, chocolate, instant coffee and packet sandwiches for the next few days, all of which will be consumed in the snug confines of the police van or while standing on the roadside. After the introductions, I promptly forget everyone's names, even the ones I've worked with before (I'll have to badger Sophie about that later, as she'll know). We then discuss the scene as a whole and review some of the information (for example, mobile phone data) that led the police to search this location. After the initial briefing I take myself off for a look at the plants. This is to familiarise myself with the ecology of the area and to further reassemble my mind. It's now about 9.30 and about time I woke up! Feeling a bit smug, I'm quite pleased that my car-bound assessment of the vegetation is largely correct. The grassland is actually more interesting than I'd imagined. It's quite species-rich but is sadly neglected because there has been too little grazing or cutting for hay. Tree saplings are beginning to establish, and in another decade or so the grassland will largely be gone. This really peeves me because species-rich lowland grasslands are some of our most endangered habitats, far more so than woodland, and to date we've lost over 97 per cent of them.

We decide to focus our efforts on the most likely areas for a hurried burial late at night – those most accessible from the layby and the side of the road. Even a small dead person rapidly feels very heavy when being moved, and it is rare for a person's body to be carried or dragged more than 50 metres unless the perpetrator is very athletic. We start with the ditch and adjacent vegetation running along the edge of the layby. It is about 200 metres long and 8 metres wide. It is also quite deep, in some areas well over 2 metres, and with steep sides. Not surprisingly, because it's been raining almost non-stop for about ten days, the bottom is very wet in some places.

From the roadside, the ditch looks almost attractive and the vegetation is lush. It is dotted with young trees and large bushes of hawthorn that are full of red berries. In reality, the ditch is horrible. This is mainly because a large proportion of the human population are filthy and dump almost anything they feel to be inconvenient in ditches. This is a tragedy, since ditches harbour amazing plants. One of England's rarest plants, fen ragwort (*Jacobaea paludosa*), has its last redoubt in a ditch sandwiched between a lorry-dominated layby and an arable field. There are chunks of broken vehicle, mainly bumpers and hubcaps. Lumps of builders' rubble and the odd kitchen sink reflect the ditch's history as an occasional haunt for fly-tippers. The dominant crud, however, is mountains of fast-food packaging. I start to feel pretty vicious. There is also a waft of deep foetidity, not the rich, natural compounds derived from the breakdown of leaflitter and plant matter. This pong is closer to home: it's the urine of countless lorry drivers intermixed with human faeces. Not for the first time, I've just stood in someone's crap. I sigh, proceed and thank my foresightedness in bringing my best, watertight boots. They'll need a good scrub before I get home.

I trudge back and forth through the ditch looking for tell-tale signs of a clandestine burial. Nothing, no quick win. Sophie and I catch up with each other and decide how to proceed. The area is very large, so we'll need to break it up into 10-metre sections before we focus our efforts. We start marking out the area with tape-measures and begin drawing our own preliminary maps. Her mapping focuses of the general landscape features, mine on the plants. I take a series of photographs to document the vegetation. We then start doing our more detailed examinations. Both of our heads are bowed as we scan back and forth, each contemplating the ground in our own way. I'm looking for signs of damage to the vegetation or plants that look odd or somehow out of their natural position. Every now and then we discuss whether we feel something arouses our interest. If so, a small flag is positioned next to something that might warrant further investigation. After we are done, the ground is festooned with small red flags. The flag positions are then plotted onto our sketch maps. Every area marked with a flag is then examined and marked off the list when we find no signs of purposeful disturbance. About an hour later, all the flags have been removed. One ten-metre square done, just another nineteen poo-infested sections of ditch bursting with bramble, nettles and thorn to examine. Time for an instant coffee and a bar of chocolate. If we need to go to the loo, we have to find a private space well away from the area or wait until the evening. Depending on the police force, it's not very often that a portable toilet is provided.

After our quick pitstop, we proceed with examining the remaining nineteen sections. Luckily, the further we move away from middle of the layby there are fewer signs of human disturbance and it's a lot less smelly. When we reach the twentieth, it is mid-afternoon. So far, we've found nothing significant. We squeeze in a late lunch – for me it's a cheese sandwich that has been defiled with mayonnaise. Lunchtime conversation starts off with a few grumbles about aching knees but soon turns to what we'll do next. One of the detectives has arrived, Sophie briefs him on our progress. He looks quite glum; he rather liked the look of this location and was clearly hoping for early results. We all were. There are signs of sleet on the way. We discuss what our next priorities will be.

It's clear that some of the PolSA team are itching to do something. It's not in their nature to sit waiting while some fey botanist from London looks at flowers. There is a suggestion that a small digger be brought in to 'speed things up'. Sophie goes a little pale. She does this when she's drawing on her diplomacy reserves. I sense her slight pause for breath as she calmly explains that this would not be a good idea. In my mind, I agree with her. Coming from a farming and horticultural background, I can tell when soil is carrying as much water as it can cope with. Driving heavy vehicles over saturated clay soils is asking for trouble. It will become a quagmire. The site will become horrendous and potentially dangerous to work in. Carefully, Sophie explains that heavy machinery could cause significant damage to any evidence, especially the woman's remains. Thankfully, the idea is shelved.

The three main areas left to search are two large fields and the hedges which surround them, a small stream which is surrounded by dense thickets of very spiny blackthorn hedge and the plantation woodland. From the information provided by witnesses, the police favour the fields and hedges. The PolSA team have been on site for several days, and the lead PolSA tells us they have already 'taken a look' along the hedgerow bordering the stream and dug a few pits. Once more, Sophie's skin pales, and I can guess what's coming next. She asks the PolSA if there are any sketch maps of where they've dug. There aren't, but he claims he knows exactly where they all are. As it turns out, they are not quite so sure, and we spend some time locating all of their pits.

It would be easy to roll one's eyes at this. But, spare a thought for the PolSA team. They've been crammed in the back of a police van for several days. Most of them have probably never worked a (suspected) crime scene in the countryside and, from what I've seen, they get very little training that would equip them for scenes such as this. Most serious crimes occur in and around the home, the street or the workplace; potential crime scenes in the countryside are rare and so police staff often don't get much opportunity to work in places like this. From what I've gleaned, they're pretty much expected to train on the job when it comes to atypical scenarios. Nevertheless, undocumented activity at a scene is not entirely helpful. Sophie and I will have to re-examine the dig sites to ensure that nothing is missed.

To get a better view of the inside of the hedge and the banks of the stream, I clamber down onto the stream bed. Despite the heavy rain of the last few days, it's shallow in this section. The stream is quite narrow but steep-banked. It is obvious that getting the body of a murder victim down here at two in the morning would be very hard, but not impossible. Therefore, I must continue checking. After several hundred metres, my phone beeps. I take it out to check my email, because I'm also dealing with an enquiry about another murder. There's nothing of importance and as I go to put my phone away, I stumble slightly and drop my phone in the stream. Whilst simultaneously swearing a lot my hand darts into the icy water and retrieves the phone. Amazingly, it continues to work and the PolSAs get a small laugh at my expense.

Sophie and I then move up and down the length of the hedgerows bordering the stream. During our examination we locate the earlier signs of the PolSA team's excavations. One or two additional mounds of earth are obviously associated with badger and fox activity. These are also checked. By this time, I have finished my work on this section and I have a little spare time. I write up my notes on the morning's work. When my notes are finished, I start chatting to one of the PolSAs over a brew. He's ex-forces and has seen active service. For some reason our conversation wanders onto restraint techniques. He happily shows me how he can rapidly immobilise me with one or two deft manoeuvres. It's quite fun and interesting. He gently shows me on my body how much they can hurt. They bloody well do. Obviously satisfied by my response he offers to show me more. I tell him to sod off and he laughs. Coffee break over. Sophie catches up with me from her examinations along the edge of the stream or hedgerow. She's rather muddy from having been working on her hands and knees and has found nothing.

By now, it's getting dark and it's time to call it a day. There is one area that we'll need to examine more carefully. It's near the culvert that takes the stream under the road and there's a largish bank of bare silt that would be easy to dig into. On the way back to the hotel Sophie and I talk about the day's efforts and lament the lack of a breakthrough.

The hotel is out of town and rather isolated on a very drab main road, so there will be no mooching for me tonight. We inform the receptionist that we'll be staying for dinner. There are five of us, as we have been joined by some of the PolSA team who are too far away from home to travel back easily the following morning. I find the evening rather fun, as it gives me an opportunity to learn more about life working for the police. There is a fair amount of sharing tales of past cases they've worked on and I get to blather on a bit about plants and how they can be used in crime-scene work. After dinner, the laptops come out and we ensconce ourselves in a quiet corner of the bar and talk more about the case and the scene we are working on. We review our actions from the day and discuss how to proceed.

One thing is certain: a sub-aqua team will need to search the culvert under the road, since it is very long and dark and probably quite dangerous. A couple of pints of beer are consumed and we chat and get to know each other a bit more. Even through I've been out for many years, I always have a sense of anticipation at these moments. Being stuck in an isolated hotel with a homophobe is not my idea of fun. Luckily, no one gurns when I mention my partner and the evening passes nicely. The PolSAs gradually share more with me about the toughness of their lives, the long hours, the violence and the difficulty of maintaining family relations. This could easily descend into a bit of a boozy session; so luckily we all decide it is time to head to bed.

The following morning is very brisk indeed; there has been quite hard frost and the sky bubbles with heavy grey clouds. No doubt more sleet and rain is to come. I have a very nice piece of light silk that I use as a scarf and sometimes when it's really cold, I wrap it around my midriff. I'm very fond of it and I've had it for years. I used to work in the now defunct and greatly missed London Lesbian and Gay Centre. One of the weekly highlights was the marvellous South Asian Shakti disco. My scarf was left behind by one of the drag queens and I laid claim to it. I gain a little quiet pleasure that I'm bringing some South Asian glamour to a roadside verge in the north of England.

The first task of the day is to examine the fields. The police have already done some work on exploring potential burials in the grass. They are a little vague on where they've been working, and it takes us a while to find every location. Clandestine burials in grassland can be quite tricky to work with. If the person digging knows what they're doing, signs of disturbance in grassland can fade very quickly. The police have commissioned an aerial survey of the fields using a drone equipped with specialist radar-like equipment that can penetrate the ground and detect anomalies. We stare at the maps trying to decide which of the coloured patches are the most likely locations for a clandestine burial. Some appear too small to be a burial site. There is no information to suggest that the perpetrator dismembered the body, therefore we are looking for a fairly large area of disturbance. But, we cannot rule out that the suspect has accomplished something unexpected.

Even though the police and forensic anthropologists have a great deal of experience in predicting human behaviour, sometimes the unexpected can happen. A fellow forensics specialist once told me the extraordinary story of a man who killed a rival. The police were confident that he had done it, but they were unable to locate the body. The absence of a body does not prevent a trial going ahead but a person's remains often holds a lot of evidence about how the crime was committed. This sort of information can be vital not only in securing a conviction, but it is also of great importance at sentencing. When the judge is sentencing, they will take into consideration evidence presented to the court about the severity of injuries sustained by the victim and the best way to understand this is from an examination of the body. The police searched the area where they believed the man had disposed of his rival but were unable to find disturbed ground anywhere that was sufficiently large for an adult body. However, there was one small area, approximately the size of a large manhole cover, that appeared to have been dug. Having little expectation of finding anything, they reluctantly agreed to let a forensic anthropologist examine it. After half an hour or so a shallow pit had been excavated and there was no sign that they had reached undisturbed ground. The pit continued to go downwards and ended up being several feet deep. There was nothing to be seen. The anthropologist then noticed that the soil was loose on one side of the pit. There was a small cavity going sideways. Inside, the remains of the victim were found, folded into a foetal position. Amazingly, witness evidence suggested that the perpetrator had dug the hole in less than 2 hours. The whole effort required not only great skill but considerable strength.

Small excavations are sometimes also used to bury personal artefacts or blood-soaked clothing. We will need to check every single anomaly identified by the aerial survey. I start my own assessment of the whole field while Sophie and the PolSA team concentrate on an area near the road that the police feel is a likely contender. I scour the hedge lines looking for signs of disturbance. The leaves have largely fallen off the trees and bushes and in many areas the ground cannot be seen. The crime occurred several months earlier and the delay in examining the area does not help. Reading the vegetation for signs of disturbance gets harder and harder as time progresses.

It takes me a couple of hours just to walk around the field perimeter, which is several-hundred yards long. Much of the field margin is largely impenetrable, as years of neglect have resulted in large patches of developing bramble and hawthorn scrub. Around them are tall stands of vegetation dominated by nettle and rosebay willowherb (*Epilobium angustifolium*). I can see that none have been disturbed by people since at least the beginning of the year, as there are no tell-tale signs of previous damage and regrowth. A person lugging a dead weight through this in the middle of the night would leave quite a trail.

I start to concentrate on the shorter grass in the centre of the field and the anomalies that the aerial survey picked up on. Some of the anomalies are deep within the scrub. They are certainly not recent, they are most likely ghosts of long passed agricultural activity such as the position of water troughs for animals. I note the anomalies and my observations on my sketch map and in my notes. Much of the field is dominated by ankle to thigh-high grass, sedges and rushes – grass-like plants that are often associated with damp ground. Some of the anomalies in this area turn out to be pieces of agricultural or domestic debris. One is a pile of thick grassy material that looks like it is the remnant of the previous year's mowing. The field is now largely only used by dog walkers, and someone has been trying to keep an open path. Overall, I'm left with about two or three locations that look interesting, but I'm not hopeful. They just don't look right.

As an early, chilly dusk falls, we have completed all our examinations and found nothing. We retire to the hotel and the very basic menu. Garlic mushrooms again for me. The work does not stop. After a quick shower we meet in the hotel to discuss the day's progress and revisit elements of the case that might be of relevance during the following days. And John Smith's beer – I hate the stuff but it's that or Foster's. It's fair to say that we are all beginning to feel a little despondent. The further we move away from the layby the less likely it is that we will find anything.

The following day will require a slightly different approach. We will be working in the plantation, where it's not possible to use aerial surveys or radar effectively. The branches of the trees block the view and the roots of trees create such a complex pattern that it is very hard to identify anomalies. It will be entirely down to the botany and the experience of Sophie. During the evening we learn that one of the PolSA team has been chatting to a local farmer, who is willing to rent the police his small digger to assist in the search. My inner sarcastic voice whispers, 'How kind. That's a nice little earner for the farmer!'. We sense that this time we are not going to win the argument, the digger will be on site soon.

Botanically speaking, the plantation is a dull affair. Most of the ground is covered with ivy (*Hedera* spp.). There are a few signs of spring flowers, mainly bluebells, doubtless non-native hybrids (*Hyacinthoides × massartiana*; the × indicates the plant is a hybrid) which often occur as a garden escape near towns and villages. Their now dead, pale-straw-coloured stems are at least six months old. Under the trees, there are few other plants: nettles, brambles and the occasional wood avens (*Geum urbanum*). I'm not going to get any botanical thrills here.

It is necessary to do a more thorough mapping of the woodland than we did with the field. Mapping woodlands can be tricky, as it's quite hard to keep sight of fixed points. These are locations from which all measurements and sketches are taken. They should be a large and permanent structure in the landscape, such as a big, mature tree or a telegraph pole. Even so, keeping track of a fixed point in a wood can be hard. Like the layby, we divide the plantation up into 10-metre squares and there are over 40 of them.

We concentrate on the areas nearest the road and the field boundary. There has been a lot of human activity, and my mapping soon becomes very complex. The shyer travellers from the main road have used the woodland margins as a more decorous latrine than the layby itself. In other areas, less socially conscious members of the nearby housing estate have used the wood as a dumping ground. It always amazes me that some gardeners, who we would expect to want to beautify the world, are quite happy to dump their rubbish all over the countryside. And it's not just gardeners; it's another popular spot for fly-tippers with more builders' rubble and domestic white goods. All of these will have to be documented and searched.

My mapping takes hours and I'm quietly chuffed with the result. Over the graph paper's 1-millimetre lines, I have drawn an intricate patchwork of circles, cross hatching and shading to depict the areas of disturbance and the surrounding vegetation. I've ended up with over 40 locations which need to be examined. We may not have enough flags. Each one of these needs to be photographed before we can proceed with examining them. Luckily, we are able to examine and exclude nearly all of them very quickly. In most cases, the dumped rubbish is lying on the surface and it very easy to confirm that no digging has taken place and only a few of the piles of brash are large enough to hide a body under.

Surprisingly, we are finished as the light fades. We've been on site for three days and have found nothing. We collect our bags from the hotel and head for home. There is disappointment at not being successful, because it would have been wonderful to know that the family and friends of the woman would be able to say goodbye properly. On returning to our offices, we will have to complete writing up our notes and our mapping will be collated and archived, along with the photography, as they may be important in the future. They are a record of what we have done and how we have done it. If, by some misfortune, we overlooked the victim's remains, there will be a record of how that came to pass.

7

Grave Searches, Canines
and Cadaverine

Our three days at the layby were part of a much larger ongoing investigation. I visited the area several times afterwards to search other parts of the site and to assess further locations along the main road. The case is the longest and most complex case I have worked on. The police were there much longer. Several days at a crime scene is like doing two hard weeks work. Luckily, I can step away from the intensity of the experience; unlike the police, who are obliged to do this constantly. Searching for the dead is one of the more difficult and painstaking tasks for people investigating crime. Shortly after our first visit, the police used the digger to scrape the surface of part of the field that we had searched. Disappointingly for them and the family of the deceased, nothing was found. Quietly and rather selfishly, I was relieved. It would have been professionally embarrassing if I had overlooked something.

The police's use of the digger does reveal a little of what I feel is rather a boys-with-toys urge. The police don't overtly or even consciously distrust environmental forensic examination using disciplines like botany or soil science but there appears to be an ingrained urge to do something dynamic using large pieces of equipment. 'Sledgehammer' and 'nut' springs to mind. While I was working on a different case, this urge resulted in a degree of farce and was potentially dangerous. Like the layby case, we were searching for a murder victim but, in this case, they had been missing for almost a decade. A witness statement suggested that the burial occurred in one of several low-lying fields next to the very boggy source of a small stream. The ground surrounding the stream was like a giant blancmange – even walking on it was very tricky. Despite our concerns, the police enlisted the help of a local farmer who was obviously fascinated by the proceedings and wanted to impress. The farmer brought on a small digger which promptly got stuck and almost tipped over into the swamp. This then required extracting, so a small tractor was deployed to pull it free, that too got stuck. We ended up with the rather ludicrous sight of three vehicles tied to one another in a long chain being used to extract the digger. By the time this was done, much of the site was churned into a mud-spattered mess. I'm recalling this not to lampoon those involved, although they probably deserve it a bit, but to highlight the unfortunate human tendency to seek complex solutions to simple problems. Some wellies and a little patience would have sufficed.

The police use confidential techniques developed to unpick the thinking of those who seek to hide contraband such as drugs or illegal arms. These techniques are based around studying how people behave in the landscape when they are attempting to conceal their acts. Investigators will take into account features in the landscape such as water bodies, trees, the profile of the land and light sources as a means of assessing the locations of likely clandestine burials. Not surprisingly, they are not keen on the details of this knowledge and experience being shared, and most search planning work is done by the police forces using their own resources.

It is now several years since I first worked on the layby case and the police continue to search. Thankfully, the murderer is now behind bars, because his crime was truly awful. As I mentioned earlier, this investigation was highly reliant on witness statements. Despite their best efforts, witnesses can easily forget some information when they're under stress. We tend to forget that committing serious crimes like murder is very stressful. The mind of the perpetrator is racing to find solutions to the predicament they are in. Without knowing it, they will focus and remember certain details, while others will be lost or transformed. Also, in many cases, the suspect may come to believe that it is not in their best interests for the victim to be found, or they derive a sense of power or pleasure in misleading. The potential unreliability of witness information can lead to the search being conducted in the wrong place.

I think about the layby murder victim quite a lot. It saddens me that she is still out there alone and that the family can never properly grieve. I feel we tried our best; each section of verge and layby considered to be a likely location for her remains has been documented, searched and, where necessary, excavated. Hopefully, one day some turn of events may help the police succeed, and I dearly hope that I am there to see it.

Criminals often resort to using burial grounds as a means of hiding their activities. Graves and their associated monuments are sometimes seen as ideal spots to sequester stolen goods, guns, drugs or murder victims. Graveyards are convenient, as virtually every habitation with more than a few houses has at least one. Imagine you have just killed someone. It is two o'clock in the morning and you need to hide your victim quickly. The local graveyard is likely to be a good contender. Not only do most graveyards have an abundance of trees to provide cover, they are generally poorly lit and don't have many (living) people in them after dusk. Also, they usually don't have too many windows overlooking them, as most people have an aversion to looking over graveyards. The abundance and diversity of stone tombs and ornaments also provide plentiful opportunities to hide from view and to dispose of your victim.

There is also a belief that, because of the plenitude of dead bodies, it is harder for cadaver dogs to locate victims in graveyards. Cadaver dogs are used widely, and not just for murder investigations. They are used for locating missing persons who are believed dead, especially in natural disasters such as tsunamis or earthquakes and in atrocities such as terrorist attacks. The dogs, usually Alsatians or Labradors, learn to recognise the scent of decaying humans, in a training process that takes up to two years. This can be done using a variety of scent sources: some are artificial, others are of natural origin such as donated human bones or placenta.

It is not clear whether the background odour of the legitimately buried does disguise the smell of the clandestinely interred. We still do not know a lot about how the volatile organic compounds (VOCs) that create the smell, permeate the soil and become airborne, react to different soil conditions and other environmental factors such as air temperature and humidity. A body and its associated microbial community give off hundreds of VOCs, the most well-known of these being putrescene, cadaverine, skatole and indole.

At low concentrations skatole and indole have a pleasant flowery odour and the synthetic version of skatole is used to manufacture some perfumes as a substitute for civet or combined with sandalwood. It can also be used to flavour food such as ice cream and may be added to cigarettes. For those keen on gardening, every time you breathe in the heady scent of jasmine or orange blossom you breathe in skatole. Many insect groups are attracted to skatole, particularly flies, beetles and male euglossine bees, also known as orchid bees. The plants produce skatole as a means of attracting these pollinators. The hope that a legitimately buried body, six-foot deep and contained in a casket, is sufficient to disguise the odour of a body much closer to the surface is probably optimistic; nevertheless, people try.

Cadaver dogs, like people, are fallible. Several years ago, I was working on a case where we were looking for the remains of a woman who was believed to have been murdered by her boyfriend and buried in a park near their home. After several hours of examining the park with Sophie and locating areas of interest, it was decided that the search could be made more efficient by using cadaver dogs. Each dog is only allowed to work for a limited amount of time before they become tired or distracted, so they were brought out on rotation to ensure our time was used most efficiently.

Satisfyingly, the cadaver dogs responded strongly to several of the areas that Sophie and I thought most promising. There remained a degree of doubt, so after some discussion it was decided that the most promising locations should be probed with an auger. Essentially, an auger is a corkscrew that is a foot or two in length. It is driven into the ground to release more VOCs and thus make detection by the cadaver dogs more likely. This form of probing is controversial because it is not entirely clear that the auger has the desired effect, since much of the volatility of the compounds appears to be dependent upon environmental conditions such as temperature and humidity. More importantly, there is a significant risk that evidence, or the remains of the person being searched for, could be damaged by the auger. Unsurprisingly, Sophie was not a fan of this course of action, and strenuously advised against it. Being part of a criminal investigation requires considerable patience and diplomacy. Quite often decisions are made elsewhere, and it is necessary to accept these decisions and proceed as best you can, something both Sophie and I find quite hard at times. We are not diplomats.

Reluctantly, we acknowledged the decision to proceed with the auger. Assiduously, we noted the discussion's contents, our viewpoint and the outcome. After all the locations had been augered, we waited half an hour for the gases to rise from the newly exposed soil. Another of the dogs was brought out. The dog reacted strongly at one of the sites, and we agreed to proceed with excavation. Up until that point, we had been informally examining the area, but it was now decided to declare a potential crime scene. Declaring an area as a potential crime scene elevates the level of attention to detail and documentation. A cordon is set up and only those of us needed to work directly on the scene are allowed within. Naturally, full protective clothing is worn.

Most of us who work in forensics share a pet hate about crime-scene dramas, the regularity with which the un-besuited lead investigator character saunters under the perimeter barrier and into the tent protecting the remains of the murder victim. Sometimes, they'll even stoop and pick something up, often with a pen! There is no way this would happen in a well-managed crime scene. The crime-scene manager would eviscerate the offender. For a start, no matter who you are, you have to declare your identity and log in; the officer on duty at the perimeter will insist upon that. And, before you approach the deposition scene, you'll be expected to don a protective suit.

Those white disposable, all encompassing, rustling romper suits serve a very important purpose. They protect a crime scene from contamination from other sources. To a certain extent, they also protect the wearer. When

I'm putting on a protective suit I feel a mixture of being rather important and slightly ridiculous. The suits are rather taxing to wear. Your hearing becomes muffled so you spend quite a bit of time trying not to say 'what?' or 'pardon, I can't hear you?'. This is exacerbated by the constant rustling of the fabric. Because I wear glasses when I'm working, my glasses get steamed up by my breath that is redirected by the face mask. In winter, the extra layer can be quite a blessing, especially if it's windy. In summer, the suits are purgatory – clamminess abounds.

We were now working on a potential crime scene, so we spent quite a bit of time documenting the location in more detail with photographs, sketch maps and copious notes recording our activities. Sophie started to scrape away the soil surface with her small hand trowel. All the soil needs to be moved to one side and carefully checked for potential evidence. Very quickly she found the edges of a previously dug hole, known as a 'pit', approximately 40 cm by 30 cm. I have worked very closely with forensic archaeologists and anthropologists when they've excavated a pit, and I am always amazed by their ability to detect the difference between undisturbed soil and soil that has been dug but is now heavily compacted. Their wrists are ultrasensitive, and each movement of the trowel defines the edge of the pit without damaging it. Quite often I will need to excavate roots, and I have attempted to emulate this action; it is quite an art.

After half an hour or so, a small pink piece of towelling came into view. Even for experienced detectives, crime scene managers and other members of the team, this is a tense and emotionally draining time. There is a degree of controlled excitation in the air; as professionals, we all hope to find the victim and as ordinary, caring people there is trepidation. It's not nice to be able to confirm that someone has been murdered, because there is always a hope that they have simply gone missing. The smallness of the pit and gradually revealed dimensions of the towel bundle led us to consider the likelihood that the victim had been dismembered.

From all perspectives, dismembered remains are far more challenging than an entire body. An investigating team will have to locate every part of the person's remains, which can be time consuming and extremely hard to accomplish. This is especially true if more than one location is involved. Human remains damaged by dismemberment are also more complex to interpret, as damage to bones and tissue may have arisen at the time of death or afterwards. Quite often human remains are damaged by animals such as rats or foxes. Understanding how this damage occurred is often essential in understanding a case. And, of course, it is very hard for the living to bear the news about what befell their loved one before their death.

As more of the towel became visible, we could also see strands of blonde hair emerging from the edge of the bundle. There was a quick scramble to verify the colour of the hair of the victim prior to her disappearance. No one was quite sure. Sophie was now finally ready to lift the bundle from the pit and start the process of unwrapping. At this point, we were all feeling extremely tense. As the towelling was gently pulled back, we all felt a draining wave of disappointment. Within the bundle lay a small dog. There was a realisation that we had failed and, rather comically, that we had just spent several hours digging up someone's pet dog.

Sadly, we were unable to return the dog to the grave. The dog's remains had to be taken away and destroyed. We could not reinter the remains because the park was quite a crime hotspot and leaving the dog in place could have caused problems and wasted resources for future investigations. Sophie had two final tasks to do before we proceeded. First, she ensured there was nothing buried beneath the dog's remains, so she continued excavating until the base of the pit was reached. Nothing was found. This needed to be done because there have been cases of criminals burying human remains beneath animal bodies or under legitimate burials. Sophie also had to make detailed notes of the excavation. This may seem unwarranted but even negative results must be accounted for. There is always the possibility that we made an error and missed vital evidence (or the victim). Documenting our activities is key to demonstrating that the work was undertaken to the best of our abilities. As this tale demonstrates, even experts and cadaver dogs are fallible. But we all learn from these occasions.

*

Several years ago, I was suffering from some self-doubt about my ability to do forensic casework. One of the more challenging things about what I do is that, in many respects, I'm never in familiar territory. Each case is very different. Not only are the awful things that people do to each other varied but the circumstances under which they occur are always unique. This scenario is amplified when the casework is outside of the built environment. This is simply because the natural world is very complex. The landscape and the plants that I work with are nearly always different in some way or another. This can lead to moments of uncertainty when approaching a new scene. I found myself feeling that there was an expectation that I was arriving, fully prepared and capable of resolving the burning issue that the investigating team needed investigating. And sometimes that led me to feel less than qualified to do the job. As is often the case, these sort of emotions are born of a degree of insecurity, because it can be very challenging to be surrounded by very experienced people, especially at a crime scene! Sophie very kindly and effectively told me that I was wrong to feel that way. She pointed out that most detectives will work on a serious crime involving landscape and plants only once or twice in their careers. Most serious crime happens in the built environment and most murder victims are found within a few days of their death at most. By the time that I was having my wobble in self-confidence, I had worked on around twenty serious crime cases of this nature, so, relatively speaking I was an old hand! As I have become more experienced, these feeling have waned, but I am careful to not allow them to be replaced by hubris. By degrees, over the last few years I have started to feel the odd wince when I experience something that I don't feel is best practice. Part of the problem for most police forces and, to a lesser extent, some forensic service providers, is that because of the relative rarity of these sort of cases they are not always geared up to deal with them.

It came as quite a shock to me that many churchyards in England and Wales do not have accurate information on where the burials in their grounds are. This is not entirely surprising for those that are hundreds of years old but, for more recent burials, it is. In typical British style, the requirements concerning burial grounds are a patchwork of national law,

Church of England tradition, local authority rules and the best practice of the many other secular and religious bodies. Ordinarily, only local authorities are required to maintain maps of burial grounds. This seems to me to be rather extraordinary and deeply unhelpful for those of us working on a criminal investigation.

Several years ago, a 'cold case', the murder of a teenager who was believed to have been killed by a paedophile, was reactivated following credible information from new witnesses being given to the police. One of the main search areas was a local church. The burial ground of this church was several hundred years old and apart from the very recent burials, the church authorities were unable to provide the police with any accurate information concerning late-twentieth-century burials. As a consequence, the police had to assume that the whole burial ground was a potential location for the teenager's remains.

The police and the specialist forensics company they were working with requested that I assist in locating the victim's remains. Vegetation can be a useful tool in helping locate murder victims in such cases, but there are limitations. Often, signs of disturbance diminish and are lost after two to five years. This case was approximately thirty years old. On top of that, graveyards are usually quite actively maintained and there is a lot of continuous activity. People visit loved ones and plant flowers or small shrubs on their graves. Maintenance staff mow lawns and prune trees and shrubs. And, if the grounds are still in use, burials occur. All of this leads to a very complex patchwork of human activity and it can be very hard to identify signs of illegal activity. I spent a rather despondent day hoping to find signs that may be helpful. I was unsuccessful. As far as I know, the victim has still not been recovered and their family remains in ghastly limbo.

As part of another case, I spent three days walking back and forth across a very large Victorian-era local authority cemetery. I was assisting the police in looking for a person who had been tortured and murdered by a criminal gang. It was believed that the victim had been killed within the last six months. Those few days were tiring. It was mid-summer, absolutely boiling hot and incredibly time-consuming work. Map in hand, I examined over 10,000 graves looking for signs of disturbance. If the victim was in the cemetery, there was a reasonable likelihood that they would be found. Most of the graves were marked by simple headstones. For these graves I looked for signs of damage to the turf or movement of gravel-chip dressings on the surface of the grave. Each time I noted anything of interest it would be documented on my copy of the cemetery burial maps.

A small minority of the graves were grander and either consisted of single, large stone slabs or more elaborate chest tombs. Chest tombs are sometimes favoured by criminals because, depending upon the weight, the covering slab can be slid to one side and replaced once the contraband or victim has been placed within. One of the tasks for the search team was to examine these tombs for signs of disturbance. More obvious signs such as recent breakages of the slabs or scratch marks made by tools such as crowbars were also marked up on our maps. And I applied some of my curious botanical wizardry by looking at damage done to the plants.

Ivy (*Hedera* spp.) is one of our most abundant and ecologically important wild and cultivated plants. It is also immensely valuable as a nectar source for a wide range of invertebrates. Ivy often abounds in graveyards, covering the ground, tree trunks and stone memorials. By our standards, ivy is a very odd plant. It is the only wild plant of these islands that is strongly dimorphic in growth, meaning that ivy grows in two distinct and different stages. The juvenile stage is made up of long, slender, sinuous stems that are normally pressed closely to the surface upon which they grow. These stems have short, fine roots along one side of the stem. These roots are normally firmly attached to whatever they touch and help the plant climb. The adult stage lacks this sinuous growth and is more bushy, akin to an ordinary shrub. This stage bears branches with flowers and ultimately, fruit. Flowering ivy is one of the best food sources for a very wide range of insects; let it bloom!

The juvenile ivy stems are the most useful to me. It is impossible to move an ivy-clad grave slab without either breaking the stems or detaching them. Even if an attempt were made to reposition the slab carefully, I would see the tell-tale signs. To us natural historians, it is well known that old graveyards are havens for wildlife and that tombstones are often particularly good habitats. They can harbour a rich community of mosses, liverworts and lichens, as well as larger plants such as ferns or the delightfully fleshy navelwort (*Umbillicus rupestris*). These intricate communities also host a diverse assemblage of minute animals such as tardigrades, also known as 'little water bears'.

Not all gravestones are excellent habitats. Heavily polished marble and slate surfaces offer little in the way of a home, except for bacteria. Generally, rough-hewn limestone and granite rock offer the best range of niches on which life can take told. Most lichens, mosses and liverworts start life as small, relatively simple spores, which are most frequently spread in the environment by water or air. In most cases, each spore is less than a hundredth of a millimetre across. Most never make it to maturity; they are either killed by viruses or eaten by predators such as the voracious tardigrades. Many are zapped by the ultraviolet radiation of the sun or are desiccated.

If a spore survives and starts to grow, it will simultaneously spread in all directions across the surface, gradually getting larger. As each year and decade progresses the organism will gradually increase in size and usually develop a roughly circular outline, the youngest part on the outer edge and the oldest in the middle. In particularly old individuals the centre starts to die, and a ring will form. Very often these growth patches will form on the edge of one grave slab and grow over onto the adjoining surface, locking the vault closed with a biological seal. As with the ivy, it is not possible to slide the top of a chest tomb to one side without breaking that seal. The colony will be torn apart and it is very unlikely that the corresponding portions will align true if the top is slid back into place.

After a couple of days of mind-aching pacing back and forth, my maps were dotted with about thirty graves that I thought showed some signs of disturbance. My observations were cross-referenced with those made by the police search team and my forensic anthropology colleague. We then prioritised the most likely locations. The first grave we examined was a large Victorian chest tomb. It had quite a few indicators that made us feel we might be successful: there were recent scratch marks on the limestone, some of the ivy and adjoining vegetation was damaged and some of the concentric circles of lichen growth on adjoining slabs were broken up and no longer aligned. All of this was carefully documented.

The top slab was very heavy and required several people with strong arms and good backs to move it. The void within was bare and covered in decades-old aggregations of spiders' webs and the odd leaf that had somehow worked its way in through a crack. The floor was covered with daylight- and water-deprived crumbly soil. It had not been touched for many years. We sighed in disappointment, completed our notes and headed off to the next grave. One by one, we went through a similar process until we reached the end of our list. We found nothing. Failure.

Failure is such a harsh word, but we must live with it. Very often, my colleagues and I fail. It can be very hard to find a person and most searches end in failure. I know that the police have since searched other locations in the area, and as yet they have not found the victim of the gangland beating that turned to murder. Everyone working as part of a criminal investigation must brace themselves for failure. Whilst the phrase 'cold-case' elicits a frisson of glamour and excitement in the public, it simply means that we have failed, so far. Famous long-standing cases such as the disappearance and probable murder of the estate agent Suzy Lamplugh on the 28th July 1986 from outside a flat in Fulham in south-west London have fascinated the public but have caused immense pain to the living. Nearly 25 years after Suzy's disappearance police received information about a possible burial site near Pershore, Worcestershire. A witness recalled that they had seen a suspicious mound in the field around the time of Suzy's disappearance. The field was several miles from an abandoned military barracks which were searched in 2000 and 2001 following reports that the main suspect, John Cannan, had buried Suzy's body there. Despite searches using ground penetrating radar and the skills of two scientific specialists, nothing was found.

Finding a murder victim is often a very, very complex business. Get one element wrong and the chances of success dwindle rapidly. An obvious example of this is the dependence upon witnesses. Often these may be the perpetrator or their associates. It is usually not in their best interests to tell the truth and lead the investigating team to their victim. No matter how good the technology or the experience of the investigating scientists, if the intelligence is wrong or misleading then there is a lower chance of recovering someone's remains. But even a failure is some sort of result. Unless we have missed them, we can confirm that the victim is not at that location. And so, the search continues ...

8
Pollen and Spores

Within popular TV dramas and novels, the presence of plant pollen on a suspect's clothing is often used as a way of connecting them to a victim or a crime scene. Of course, it's not always as simple as that; pollen has its strengths and weaknesses in the forensic environment. To understand these strengths and weaknesses, it is necessary to learn a little about what pollen is and how it works. Pollen is a word that many of us are familiar with, especially those with allergies such as hay-fever. Even so, most people are probably unaware of how important pollen is. Without it, our world would grind to a halt. Most plants on the planet are dependent upon it for reproduction, this is because pollen is the plant equivalent of sperm. Without pollen, the embryos in flowers will go unfertilised and there will be no seed and therefore no more plants, animals, food or people. From an allergy point of view, most plant pollens don't contribute to hay-fever. Generally speaking, plants with wind-pollinated flowers, such as grasses and some trees, tend to cause hay-fever and those that are pollinated by animals such as insects or birds, don't. How do you tell which is which? The wind does not have eyes, and so the flowers don't need to attract it. Therefore, the flowers of wind-pollinated plants are small and usually green. To most human eyes, they tend to merge with the leaves. Flowers pollinated by animals need to attract the animals and they do this either by scent (which we may or may not be able to detect) or bright colours.

Pollen and plant spore (some plants, such as ferns, have spores, not pollen) cells often have tough outer coatings which mean they can persist for a long time. Under the right environmental conditions, pollen grains can last in soil for thousands of years. The toughness of pollen and plant spores is down to the composition of the cell walls. The outer cell wall of pollen is largely made of sporopollenin, one of the most robust and chemically inert naturally occurring biological polymers. Because of this durability, their presence in ancient soils is one of the ways that scientists can reconstruct past climates. As the climate changes, the plant communities change and so does the pollen profile.

This persistence in the environment is the key to pollen's usefulness in forensics. The presence of pollen on a person's clothing or footwear can be used to link them to a specific location. How is this done? All plants have specific needs – some like nutrient-rich soil, others require plentiful sunshine. This means that plants are restricted to particular types of environment, or 'habitats' as they are referred to in biology. Familiar habitat types found in north-west Europe include woodlands, sea cliffs or chalk grasslands. On top of this, very few plants have a global range and even in Britain and Ireland there are not many plants that are found everywhere. These factors mean that many plants have distinct distribution patterns across our land. It is these distribution patterns that are the key to using pollen in forensics.

Pollen is a valuable tool, but it has some limitations. The pollen of plants that rely on the wind tends to be more widely dispersed in the landscape. Pollen from wind-pollinated trees like oak (*Quercus*), beech (*Fagus*) or birch (*Betula*) can be blown many miles. This can reduce the value of some types of tree pollen in forensics. But, a high abundance of oak, beech and birch pollen on a suspect's footwear will strongly indicate that they have been in or near a woodland or wooded park. However, these pollen types won't help an investigator locate where exactly in the wood or park the suspect has been. Also, the pollen of some wind-pollinated plants, such as grasses, can be quite hard to identify accurately. The reason for this is their need to be buoyant and aerodynamic; objects with sculpted, sharp-angled surfaces don't fly very well. This need for buoyancy results in pollen grains that have relatively few surface features, a bit like car air-bags. However, some windborne pollen types are quite distinctive; the pollen of pine trees (*Pinus*) was described to me and my fellow undergraduates as looking like Mickey Mouse's head in outline. The pollen grains of pines have two inflated 'ears' either side of the 'head'. The 'ears' help the pollen float in the air. On the other hand, the pollen of plants designed to attract the attention of animals like bats, birds and insects tends to be heavier and have ornately sculpted surfaces. The surface sculpting helps the grains stick together as well as to the animal that will transport the pollen to the next flower. Unlike wind-pollinated plants, the 'wasted' pollen of these plants tends to fall to the ground near the plant it came from. Also, the surface ornamentation is incredibly diverse (and very beautiful) in these plants, so much so that in many cases they are unique to individual plant species.

All the above means that it is possible to create a pollen profile that can be used to link a suspect to a specific location. A pollen profile containing widespread woodland trees like oak, beech and birch can be useful but what really helps is if there something a bit more interesting. If I were lucky enough to be looking at a pollen profile that contained the afore-mentioned trees, as well as the pollen of plants like honeysuckle (*Lonicera periclymenum*), ramsons (*Allium ursinum*), wood anemone (*Anemone nemorosa*) and yellow archangel (*Lamium galeobdolon*), I'd be really chuffed. This list would tell me straight away, that not only was the location woodland but that it was ancient woodland. This is, as you can imagine, old woodland, and by old in England and Wales we mean at least 400 years old. Not only are ancient woods old, they also tend to have lots of plant species within them, such as the plants above, and these plants are often known as 'indicator species' because they are strongly associated with particular habitat.

Ancient woodlands are old, species rich and pretty scarce. They are scarce because our ancestors cut down much of our woodland for agriculture, charcoal and timber for building houses and ships and in the last 200 years we destroyed more by building railways, cities and motorways. Nowadays only about two percent of our landscape is covered by ancient

While I'd be very happy with the preceding list, what I'd really need to make my heart go aflutter would be a true woodland specialist and rarity. Something like spiked rampion (*Phyteuma spicatum*), a relative of the garden bellflowers (*Campanula* spp.) and now very rare in England and found in fewer than ten sites. Extracting spiked rampion pollen from an exhibit would lead me to be searching the woods around Hailsham and Heathfield in East Sussex. Clearly, this example is somewhat idealised, but the underlying principal is apparent: pollen can be used to link suspects to crime scenes.

Even after death, biological material such as pollen can remain lodged on and in our bodies. Forensic researchers sometimes come up with innovative means of retrieving information. One approach is to explore the nasal cavity. We may grumble about snot when we have a cold or hay-fever, but mucus is an amazing and important substance. Far from being simply snot, mucus is a complex substance made up of salts, enzymes, antibodies and other proteins. Most of our mucus is produced in our digestive tract where it helps protect the lining from physical damage and reduces potential harmful impacts of some bacteria. It is also found in our lungs and airways. Importantly this mucus traps small particles that we may breathe in, especially viruses, fungal spores, bacteria and pollen. Not only does mucus protect us but it is a snapshot of the environment we have been in. Anyone visiting or living in our more polluted, larger cities will attest this, as a walk along any main road is likely to result in black bogeys. The inner parts of the nasal cavity are complex and very narrow in places. Gaining access to these can be challenging. To do this, it is necessary to remove the facial skin and scalp, after which the upper portion of the skull cavity is removed. The exposed areas of the inner nasal cavity are then washed, and the liquid collected. The liquid is spun in a centrifuge to concentrate the particles and the concentrated material is then mounted onto a slide and examined under a microscope. The pollen and spores can then be identified.

Several years ago, I worked on the case of a woman who had gone missing some weeks earlier. The police had a suspect – her husband. They had searched the family home and had retrieved several items including outdoor clothing, footwear and a spade. They had also searched his car and recovered further exhibits. The police also had automatic number plate recognition (ANPR) data showing that, shortly after the wife went missing, his vehicle left the rural family home and was driven for about 100 miles. The distance travelled covered at least 2 counties. The police believed it was possible that he could have left the route at one of many different points and disposed of her body.

The police sent environmental samples taken from the exhibits for analysis to several specialists. I received some vegetation fragments that proved to be inconclusive, because the fragments came from widespread lawn grasses and were unlikely, on their own, to be of significance. The soil analyses provided some fascinating information. The soil was rich in hydrocarbons. The high levels of hydrocarbons, which were associated with exhaust fumes, indicated that the vehicle had travelled through a built-up, urban location. There were also chemical traces of an unusual industrial process that was of a very limited extent in the region. In soil retrieved from some of the exhibits, pollen and spores were also recovered and identified. Most of these were of widespread grassland plants and some more common trees. There was one spore type that was particularly interesting. It was the spore of a fern that is fairly common nationally; however in the two counties in question, the plant is rare and is only found in few restricted lowland areas. Basically, across these two largely rural counties we needed to focus our efforts on areas that matched our observations. The probable deposition scene was likely to be near an open grassy habitat close to a built-up area that was associated with an unusual industrial process. In the vicinity, there would be plants of the scarce fern. The environmental information had reduced the search area from several hundred square miles to fewer than 20. My fellow scientists and I were rather chuffed with the work and were keen to pursue it further. Inexplicably, the police did not pursue this area of work and as far as I know the case remains open. Typically, after our work is done, we hear no more.

Generally, the public perception of forensic science is coloured by 'Grissom syndrome', so-called by me in honour of the character Gil Grissom from *CSI: Crime Scene Investigation*. Because of the way popular dramas are structured, investigators and specialists are portrayed as multi-skilled super-heroes. Every now and then, when it plays a major role in a murder inquiry, real botany and forensic science captures our collective attention. Sometime after I joined the Natural History Museum, a young woman, Joanne Nelson, went missing on Valentine's Day 2005. Shortly after her disappearance, her boyfriend, Paul Dyson, was charged with her murder. After a long search hampered by winter snow and cold, the police were obliged to scale down the operation. Dyson had confessed to disposing of Joanne's body, but he claimed to be unable to recall exactly where. He told the police that he'd placed her body in bin bags and then driven from Hull towards York and dumped her by a metal gate with green bottles attached.

Despite driving around large areas of east and north Yorkshire with Dyson, the police were unable to find Joanne. Examination of Dyson's clothing by a forensic botanist revealed an interesting pollen profile. Some of the pollen was of a non-native tree with a patchy distribution in England. This is the sort of botanical clue that people like me dream of – something uncommon that is large and stands out in the landscape. The pollen of the tree, western hemlock (*Tsuga heterophylla*), was found with pollen of birch, pine (*Pinus*) and the spores of polypody fern (*Polypodium* spp.).

At this point, the police team and the forensic botanist needed to enlist the help of amateurs. The word amateur often has connotations of unskilled or inexpert. Not in this case. The amateurs the team needed the help of were members of the Botanical Society of the British Isles (now called the Botanical Society of Britain and Ireland). The BSBI is one of the oldest natural history organisations in the world, whose roots go back to 1836. It is an organisation of committed and expert people who know the wild plants of these islands better than most. Much of what we know about our wild plant life is based on BSBI expertise. Indeed, various parts of our economy are driven in part by this knowledge – agriculture, conservation, national parks and planning decisions all have BSBI expertise embedded within. In a system devised by a man called Hewett Cottrell Watson in 1852, every area of Britain and Ireland has a person, the vice-county recorder, who is responsible for collating and verifying information on the native and non-native wild plants of that area. I am recorder for vc 21, the historic county of Middlesex. The biggest English county, Yorkshire is so large that it is broken up into five vice-counties.

One of the things we recorders do is compile botanical records and maps and it was botanical maps compiled by the BSBI that enabled the investigating team to narrow their search. These maps showed that western hemlock was restricted to a few locations in that part of Yorkshire. A few days after focusing the search around the map, Detective Superintendent Ray Higgins, who was leading the investigation, was driving to meet one of the search teams near Brandsby, when he and Detective Constable Phil Gadd saw the gate as described by Dyson. Later, when being interviewed by reporters, Higgins described how they 'were driving round and saw this gate – it had everything. We looked at each other and said, 'This is it.' A path from the gate, surrounded with green bottles, led into a wooded area.' The officers stopped the car and, after a brief search in the wood, they found the partially uncovered remains of Joanne. The investigation was a success, and Dyson was found guilty. The discovery of Joanne Nelson's body might not have happened for many years without the expertise of trained and experienced botanists working alongside the detectives, particularly as Brandsby is not between Hull and York where the original search was concentrated.

9
Looking Anew

The interest of us botanists, like other human beings, is often aroused by the beautiful or the rare. We can tend to be less interested in the mundane or commonplace. Most of us would rather be looking at ancient chalk grassland full of orchids instead of nettles covered in vomit and urine in an alleyway by a mortuary. Surprisingly, this particular alleyway is one of my favourite botanical sites in London; it's fair to say that my interest in urban botany and forensics has rather warped what I find interesting! The nettle here is no ordinary nettle, it is membranous nettle (*Urtica membranacea*), a recently and accidentally introduced non-native species from the Mediterranean region. It arrived on these shores as seed in the soil of large container-grown plants imported from southern Europe. Owing to all nettles' proclivity towards nitrogen-rich environments, the plant was very much at home amongst the pigeon poo and puke. These effluvia from the bodies of animals are very rich in nitrogen. My years botanising in London have primed me to look at wild plants very differently to how I otherwise would have done, a way that would help me greatly in later years when I started doing crime-scene work.

After completing my PhD at the University of Reading in 2002, I started volunteering at a local nature reserve in central London. Camley Street Natural Park is an important site, a tiny fragment of the natural world in the midst of the glamourous, people-centric and nature-blind redevelopment of the King's Cross area. Camley Street taught me a lot. Even though I had lived in London for most of the previous decade, I'd rarely paid attention to its natural environment, mainly because I'd become involved in the gay scene and activism. The park was managed by the London Wildlife Trust and later, when I needed a job, my time volunteering at Camley Street proved invaluable. The London Wildlife Trust, on behalf of the Great London Authority, needed botanists to travel around London doing surveys of all the public space they could access. For two years I cycled across miles of London documenting, mapping and learning about its wildlife, landscape and history. I recorded the plant life, and the presence of amenities, bins or excessive dog-fouling, with the intention of documenting the often negative changes that had occurred. Many of London's biologically diverse brownfield (former industrial) sites have been lost to development while others are becoming smothered by invasive non-native species.

At each site, I would draw up a sketch plan and list the plants present, as well as the faeces and litter. The sketch maps would be drawn up using mapping software and the other information compiled into a database. To get an understanding of change, we had to resort to an old series of black-and-white photographic aerial images taken of London some 20 years earlier. Not only did The GLA Habitat Survey generate excellent information on the state of the capital's natural world, but it also provided important information used in planning applications and strategic planning by London's borough authorities. Sadly, it was later scrapped.

Now I use a very similar approach to inform my assessment of changes in the landscape when doing forensic work. The huge advances in technology mean that it is possible to draw upon a wealth of online mapping tools, street views and aerial imagery to assess change. The resolution of many of these images is sufficiently clear that I am often able to identify not only individual trees and shrubs, but the species they are likely to be. These images and street-view images are very helpful in developing a pre-scene visit understanding of what I am going to encounter. I can start to identify areas of interest that I would like to examine in more detail or draw up a preliminary list of the plant species present. This can be very useful in guiding my response to the police and the forensic companies I work with.

As helpful as these images are, they are no substitute for examining the plants directly. Non-botanists are often amazed that apparently identical plants are not the same species. An example of this are birch trees. Most people are familiar with birch; their silvery white stems are easily recognisable and found widely in our gardens, woods and heathlands. Many of us are so familiar with the word birch, that it hardly registers that this single word describes about 100 different tree species worldwide. There are two native species of birch (*B. pendula* and *B. pubescens*) found in our lowlands and a scarce, dwarf mountain species (*B. nana*, nana means small) which is largely confined to the Scottish Highlands. Things get more complicated in our gardens. Alongside the native lowland species, several other introduced species are also grown. The only way some of these species can be identified with confidence is to carefully examine their leaves and the fruit embedded within the catkins. Birch are widespread trees, common both in the wild and in gardens. Their leaves seem to get everywhere, as do their fruit and catkin scales and they are all quite often found in exhibits I examine. The fruit shape of birch is roughly the same outline as a hand-carved wooden fleur-de-lys. Each species is rather similar but also distinctly different in form, as if a different carver had created them. Identifying the fruits when they are embedded, and often badly damaged, in someone's footwear and far from the tree that they came from can be quite challenging. As a consequence, I may need to retrieve samples or take photographs of birch fruit from a deposition scene for later comparison when I am back in the laboratory.

Although I am not professionally trained as a forensic anthropologist, I have assisted in the retrieval of human remains. Under suitable professional supervision I hasten to add! It surprises people that a botanist would be assisting in this work. Part of the reason I assist is simply that the more eyes on the job, the better. If I see a bone, I'll call out to the anthropologist (or archaeologist) and let them know it's there. From a distance, all a listener would hear is the quiet calling out of 'cervical vertebra', 'scaphoid' and the other smaller bones of the body as we proceed. A place marker will then be added. Some bones, such as the smaller ones of the fingers and toes, can be very hard to find in dense leaf litter, in a wood, in December at twilight! Many a small partially decayed and decorticated twig or stone gets picked up momentarily in the anticipation that it is a weathered bone. One of the bones that can be particularly hard to find is the hyoid. This bone is unusual in that it is not in intimate connection with other bones; it is attached to the complex array of muscles that control the floor of the mouth, tongue, larynx, epiglottis and pharynx. It can also be of special interest or evidential value in some murder cases where strangulation is suspected, as a broken or damaged hyoid may be indicative of a ligature or throttling by hand.

Finding bones at a deposition scene can be harder than you may imagine, especially if the person was not buried (or if the grave is very shallow). In these cases, the remains can be disturbed by animals, natural movements of the earth, flood events or accidentally by people through digging (such as road works). Disturbance means that it can be necessary to search over a very large area to find all of a person's remains. Probably the most common cause of disturbance is by animals. They eat us.

For many of us, now highly urbanised, the idea that we can be food for other organisms is repulsive and horrifying. From the moment we die, we become a rich source of nutrition. Complex microbial communities within our digestive tract and our skin start to digest us. Especially if we are outside, within minutes of death we are found by flies and beetles, and they lay their eggs on us. We are also food for a wide range of other organisms, particularly birds and mammals.

I quite regularly lecture in public, recounting some of my experiences in forensics. I often talk about how I once worked on a case with a researcher who had conducted some fascinating reserach into the predation habits of birds and animals on human remains. She explained that, owing to the practical restrictions of being on a relatively small and very densely populated island, namely Great Britain, it was not possible to use human bodies for this work. Not entirely surprisingly, some people do not feel comfortable having human corpses near their homes. Therefore, it was necessary to use dead pigs as proxies for people. Apparently, pigs are suitable because they are a similar size and weight and have comparable fat density to humans. Forensic entomologists also use pigs as proxies for the research into the post-mortem interval. She asked me a simple question 'Which animal or bird is the first to start feeding on the remains of a large animal lying dead on the ground?'. I ask the same question when I tell this story when lecturing. Not surprisingly, birds and mammals like foxes, badgers and crows are regularly mentioned. I, like most of my audiences, didn't get the answer. It's the wood mouse (also known as the long-tailed field mouse, *Apodemus sylvaticus*). Apparently, those cute little fluffy-whiskered critters of our woods and hedgerows are rather partial to a meat snack.

My colleague and I spent quite a lot of time looking for human remains dispersed by foxes. They pose one of the more significant challenges encountered when examining a deposition scene. Most of us tend to think of ourselves as somehow apart from or different to nature. When we are dead, this false barrier breaks down. Human remains make fine pickings for scavenging animals like foxes. Luckily, like humans, foxes have behaviours that we can learn about and then predict. Foxes tend to remove a portion of the human remains, usually the extremities, and carry them to their den or a safe place. They are wary animals and are avoiding predation themselves. This means that, in most cases, the fox will have carried their food in a particular direction. Once that direction has been discovered, it is usually possible to retrieve what has not been consumed by the fox. Many people will find this the idea of being eaten by mice and foxes challenging and unsettling, but these behaviours are simply nature. We do our best to retrieve as much as possible; there may be evidence associated with the dispersed remains and clearly it is desirable to return as much as is possible to family members and friends.

Working in forensics and with other experts has certainly helped me see our landscape and natural world in a very different way. Some years ago, I was working on another gangland murder case. We were looking for the victim of a so-called punishment beating that went 'too far'. The police asked me to assist in searching an area of woodland next to a large house.

The house had already been searched without any success and the police needed to widen their efforts by searching the wood. When I arrived, the police had identified several areas within the woodland that they thought were likely locations for a clandestine burial. The woodland was dominated by tall beech trees and as I walked into one of the clearings beneath the trees, I was immediately struck by why the police had prioritised it. The space was about the size of a large school classroom and most of the vegetation was low growing. The clearing was secluded from the road, and any views were blocked by a dense three- to four-metre high growth of cherry laurel (*Prunus laurocerasus*) and holly (*Ilex aquifolium*). Both plants are evergreen, meaning that they retain their leaves all year round; this makes them ideal for clandestine activity, particularly in winter when cover is limited.

Within the clearing, none of the thinly scattered plants were more than a metre high, and much of the ground was covered by a thick mat of ivy. The space seemed perfect for disposing of a body, being secluded but with enough open ground to work without hindrance. The police were very excited by the location. Finally, they thought they had the right spot. Initially, I shared their enthusiasm, but this gradually diminished. The more I looked, the more I was convinced that the area had been purposefully cleared at least two years before the murder had occurred, and that since then nothing had disturbed the vegetation. I decided to wander around the wood to get a better feel for the vegetation. I came across several other open areas in the wood with similar dimensions and vegetation characteristics. They all appeared to have been cleared at the same time, probably with the intention of improving the habitat. Most likely, the shrubs in the clearances had been coppiced by people with woodland conservation in mind.

I returned to the main location, my confidence growing that we would not find the victim here. Even though the area was large enough to hide someone's remains, I couldn't find anywhere that was large enough to dig without disturbing the scattering of small holly bushes that were dotted about. The bushes were sufficiently small that I wondered whether some were seedlings, but on closer inspection it was clear that all the plants had been coppiced. They had been cut to the ground and had regrown, therefore most of them were once larger and considerably older than they appeared to us as we stood before them..

I explained to the CSM that I thought they were going to be unsuccessful and that the holly bushes were simply too old to have been moved without significant disturbance. He looked puzzled and asked me how that could be so; after all, they were small so they must be young? I remember having a small moment of realisation – I really did see the world in a very different way to many other people. I encouraged him to get down on his hands and knees and feel the base of the stems of one clump. After hesitating, he obliged. To this day, I still find it amazing how reluctant people are to look carefully at plants. Each stem was only one or two centimetres in diameter but were attached to a much larger stump that measured several centimetres across. I could see the realisation creep across his face – the original plants had been cut down and these shoots were the regrowth. The plants were indeed considerably older than they looked.

While I was looking at the holly bushes, I noticed something about them that I'd never noticed before. Holly doesn't have distinct buds like most other trees and shrubs growing wild in this country. Common trees like oak, birch or beech have distinctive over-wintering buds that leave a small ring of scar tissue behind once the shoot grows in spring. The easiest way to see this scar tissue is to look at the opening large sticky buds of horse-chestnut (*Aesculus* spp.). One of the forensically useful aspects these patches of scar tissue where the buds once were, is that they can help estimate the age of a branch or a sapling. Basically, start at the shoot tip and move downwards, each time you pass a ring of scar tissue, add another year. Any branch or sapling hanging over or growing in proximity to the deceased thus becomes a helpful means of estimating the minimum time period that the remains have been in position. It's a very handy and quick way of providing an initial estimate of age.

The absence of seasonal buds in holly presented me with a problem, how would I estimate how old these plants were? I spent a while pondering my problem and quietly observing. Getting to know a plant is key to understanding it. When teaching plant identification skills, I often advise botany students to spend time simply looking at the flowers, foliage and stems of a plant, ideally with a hand-lens, before jumping to conclusions about the plant's identity. It is all too easy to get fixated on the larger, more obvious features such as flower colour and overlook the important ones.

As I gazed, the penny dropped. Not all the leaves were the same size. At the tips of the shoots, the leaves were smaller; as I moved down the shoot, they gradually got larger and then they started to shrink again before once more getting larger. This pattern was repeated down the stem. I realised that, because of the cold and lack of sun, holly leaves get smaller towards the end of the growing season. As winter closes in, the shoot stops growing before resuming growth in the spring, and as summer approaches the leaves once more get larger.

I had my means of estimating how old the short holly bushes were. I tried out my new approach on all the bushes in the area. They consistently showed the same pattern of growth and supported my assessment that they were too mature to support the idea that a burial had occurred in the space occupied by them. I called the CSM over to explain my observations. He was quietly agog and initially disbelieving, but the more I showed him the plants and explained my reasoning, the more I could see the hope fade in his eyes.

As is often the case, the police felt compelled to continue with their search. I've come to accept this. All too often, even if an individual gets it, the laws of group behaviour kick in and the collective proceeds down familiar paths. Us botanists with our strange ways are a bit too much for some. The police and I surveyed the ground which was covered by an expanse of common ivy. On the ground, the stems of ivy are long and sinuous; they cover the soil in a fairly thick mat. Once again, I was convinced it would be impossible to wield a spade and cut through the stems without leaving signs of damage, of which there were none. After continuing to look for a little while, the police eventually became convinced by my observations and called off the search.

To this day, the police have never found the man. A few months after my work with them, they received information from the criminal fraternity suggesting that the man never got as far as the woodland. After being killed, his body was placed in an oil drum, sealed with concrete and then thrown in a very large lake.

10
Fragments

Hunting for the dead and examining their remains are certainly the aspects of criminal investigations that most capture the imagination of the public. However, most forensic work also involves slow and painstaking examination of exhibits. This work may not have the overt thrill and intrigue of an active crime scene, but it is where many of the real discoveries are made.

Examination of exhibits takes place in anonymous buildings scattered across the industrial estates of this country. These buildings are nothing like the brooding, atmospheric laboratory sets of many crime-scene dramas. They are very well lit and usually sparsely furnished. There is a simple reason for this. It is vitally important that nothing is lost and that every action is carefully documented. The management of this work is very time consuming and requires a great deal of concentration. The movements of exhibits within these buildings are tightly controlled. This control is extremely important, because if there is more than one crime scene associated with an investigation, then exhibits from those two locations should not be examined in the same laboratory space at the same time. The same applies for exhibits linked to victims and suspects. Preferably, they are examined on different days. Barristers are adept at pointing out that examinations were done on the same date, thus casting doubt in the mind of the jurors that the work was done separately and securely. Every single action must be recorded and documented. Poorly recorded activity can be disastrous in court and could potentially lead to miscarriages of justice.

I often need to examine footwear that has been retained as an exhibit by the police as part of an investigation. The footwear will be removed from the secure and restricted-entry evidence store. A suitable laboratory space that has been cleaned prior to use is then allocated. Benches are wiped and swabbed with alcohol. A sheet of disposable paper is then placed on the bench. Before opening the exhibit bag, I will read and check all the label information to ensure that I am examining the correct exhibit. I, or one of the laboratory's forensic examiners assigned to work with me, will then photograph the bag and the anti-tamper seals before opening the bag. The footwear will then be carefully photographed from all angles before I start to remove vegetation fragments. As I remove them, I will record where on the shoe they came from. Each individual fragment or batch of fragments will be photographed and put into packets. They will then be assigned subexhibit numbers. The numbering can get rather complicated. On completion of the work, the footwear will be returned to the exhibit bag and resealed. The seals must be signed. I really hate doing this bit, as the sealing is usually done with package tape which is a horror to write on. The same process also needs to take place for the subexhibits, and their creation documented. I often end up with a small dance going on in my head about how many subexhibits I really need and what their value will be.

There is a hierarchy to the sequence of exhibit examination. Work to isolate human DNA or gunshot residue happens first. The aim of this is to prevent the possibility of cross-contamination with DNA or gunshot residue from outside sources. There are stringent regulations on how exhibits that may harbour human DNA are handled and stored, and the forensic examiner who works alongside me has overall responsibility to ensure that the correct procedures are followed. Being a botanist, I have not worked with human DNA, but I am mindful of the risks of cross-contamination. My PhD research was based on extracting DNA from water-inhabiting fungi, and I know how easy it is for DNA cross-contamination to occur if appropriate quarantine procedures are not adhered to. It's frustrating if a PhD student gets algal and bacterial DNA in a fungus DNA sample; it's potentially catastrophic if contamination occurs in a forensic setting. Consequently, I and the people I work with are very mindful of this every time we work on material in a laboratory. To date, similar regulations do not apply to non-human DNA, but I suspect they will do in the future, especially when evidence derived from environmental DNA (eDNA) and the necrobiome (the community of organisms that live on and within us after our death) becomes used in criminal investigations.

The clothing and personal possessions of the dead are some of the most challenging exhibits. Very often they are degraded by the weather or decay, and they may be very smelly. Sometimes, I find the patterning of the stains quite hypnotic; each stain is a trace of what happened to the person. One of the more awful exhibits I had to examine was a partially destroyed suitcase. The suspect, who was subsequently found guilty of murder, had killed his victim and then placed the body in a suitcase. After disposing of the body, the perpetrator attempted to dispose of the suitcase by taking it to another location and partially destroying it by cutting it to pieces and smashing up the frame. Somehow the broken-up suitcase felt like an echo of the brutality of the murder. The attempt to destroy the suitcase may have been emphatic but it was also ineffectual; on the outer surface of the suitcase there was soil trace evidence that helped find the man guilty.

It is strange how we are affected by fragments. A novel may contain a scene that details a person in pain holding a broken and fractured relict of something or someone lost. Sometimes I find myself more affected by a pottery sherd recovered from a Bronze Age hearth in a museum than the fully restored artefact, even if the intact object is a thing of great beauty. Perhaps it is the niggling horror of the missing. For some reason, every time I see the Rosetta Stone, I feel a gnawing sensation caused by the missing parts. It drives me slightly potty – surely 'they' can find the rest.

Vegetation fragments can be very powerful tools in understanding how a crime happened, and I often receive leaf fragments from a crime scene. They are usually tiny and very badly damaged by abrasion, by the weather or the processes of decay. Each one may help tell the story of what happened, and every fragment is emblematic of a life lost or shattered.

Several years ago, I received two tiny pieces of leaf that were recovered from a victim of a violent sexual assault. After the crime, the traumatised person fled the scene, but they were unable to recall where the attack had happened. The police were hoping these fragments could be used to localise where the crime had occurred. For me, these leaf fragments shuddered with potency, they were witness to the awful event that had engulfed the victim. I carried them around the laboratory with great care, not just because of the need to treat the evidence professionally but because they had 'experienced' something awful. Through these tiny pieces of battered greenish-brown tissue I was connected to someone I would never know.

Botanists usually identify plants from whole specimens or a selective gathering that enables us to work out what the plant is. Most botanists rarely work with a torn piece of leaf that is less than a centimetre across. I tell you, it can be very difficult. The main reason is that there are a huge number of wild plants on the planet. The most recent estimates are around 320,000 species, which is a lot to remember (and realistically it cannot be done - even the best botanist has probably only got good recall of a few thousand). Obviously, not all of these grow in the wild here. The majority are tropical, but here in Britain and Ireland there are about 4,800 species of native and non-native plant growing wild.

Most of that number are of very limited occurrence or found at significant distances from the crime scene I was investigating, which left me with only a few hundred to contemplate. The reticulate patterning (think of a street map of medieval London) of the leaf veins allowed me to conclude that plant was not grass- or lily-like, as those plants have parallel veins (like the multitude of railway tracks running into Clapham Junction). This observation knocked out many other contenders. My mind started flailing around, hunting for solutions. Sometimes, this the best way to start; I don't know of any online resources or one-stop textbooks that deal with leaf fragments. I spent an hour or two pulling ideas out from the recesses of the botanical parts of my brain, forty odd years of detailed study, random observations and fleeting memories. In the back of my mind I had a strong feeling that the leaf fragments came from a tree or shrub. Needing to gain a little control and structure to my mental meanderings, I decided it was time to be a little more systematic and reached for the standard text for field botanists in Britain and Ireland, Clive Stace's third edition of the *New Flora of the British Isles* (this work has now been superseded by a 4th edition). It's quite chunky and has a reputation for terrifying the less experienced. My nickname for it is 'Regal Stace', partly owing to the purple colour theme of its cover and because of its august position in botany! I turned to the index at the back with the aim of jogging my memory by scanning through the alphabetic list of plant names: *Abies, Acanthaceae, Acanthus, Acer* ... I stopped at *Betula*, feeling a tingle of connection. Perhaps it's one of those? That would be very handy – it was a long way to *Zosteraceae*.

I paused and considered what to do next. I instinctively felt that I had the answer, but that was not enough. I would need to make sure my tentative observation withstood scrutiny in court. The best way to do this is by verifying my identification. It is possible to use online resources, as there are huge quantities of photographs of plants on the internet. Unfortunately, many are of poor quality and incorrectly labelled. Also, in most cases they are not scientifically validated. Submitting a report with a statement saying I'd compared evidence from a serious criminal investigation with images from Wikipedia is unlikely to be well received by the court, although the opposing barrister may be delighted. It is wiser to use real plant specimens from an herbarium; these have the advantage that I can compare the exhibit with the herbarium specimen under a microscope. Herbarium specimens are (or should be) identified by experienced botanists. Each specimen will have a 'determination' on them – this means that a botanist has validated the identification. I headed into the collection store and found material of British birches and started to make my comparisons. The leaf fragments were a match for one of our native birch trees, the silver birch (*Betula pendula*).

I contacted the forensics company I was working with and we arranged a scene visit with the police. As usual, when we got there, it was freezing. The search area encompassed several hundred yards of roadside verge and tracks. It was quite a bleak and isolated place on the outskirts of a small town in southern England. The most abundant trees and shrubs were hawthorns, oaks and ash. After a careful walk back and forth, I found two small areas where silver birch grew. Despite it being early winter, the fallen leaves had not been blown around in the landscape. I informed the detectives that I was reasonably confident that the sexual assault had taken place at one of these two locations.

As is so often the case, I didn't hear from the police about how the investigation proceeded.

In some cases, I am a fleeting presence in the work of the investigating team. I suspect that if the police were less busy, they would be inclined to let specialists such as myself know the outcome of an investigation. I think it simply slips their mind, since, often as not, each investigative team will be working on several cases at a time. I would very much like to hear from the police, learning from them what worked and what didn't would be very helpful. But I can't pick up the phone and badger them!

While they might not appear so, leaves are remarkably complex structures. Each leaf or, more often in crime-scene work, leaf fragment, can tell an experienced observer a lot about the origins of a plant. The main function of a leaf is to increase the surface area of a plant, which is important for two vital functions, respiration and photosynthesis. The size and form of the leaf is constrained by the environmental conditions that the plant evolved in. Predation is also a factor as leaves are often tasty! These evolutionary pressures make leaves highly diverse.

One of the more variable features of leaves are their hairs. Some plants have none, others are very hairy. The main causes for the development of hairs in plants are predation, water loss and sunlight. Obviously, predators come in all sizes and shapes. Larger grazing animals are usually deterred from eating a plant by toxicity or pain. The common stinging nettle (*Urtica dioica*) is a well-known example of this. The hairs of the plant have brittle, sharp tips that readily break off, penetrate the skin and inject formic acid, histamine and acetylcholine. As much as we grumble about the painfulness of these stings, other plants can pack a much stronger punch. Most famously, the stinging nettle's larger, scarier cousin, the gympie-gympie (*Dendrocnide moroides*), from Australia, has been known to kill horses and dogs; the pain is excruciating and lasts for days. The impact of feeding by smaller animals is reduced by having hairs as a barrier to movement. Imagine you're an aphid: you're less than a millimetre high and you need to clamber through hairs two or three times your height – it's tough going, a bit like walking through a bamboo thicket. Incidentally, by slowing you down, the hairs also make you far more vulnerable to predators such as ladybirds.

Many plants grow in arid habitats and being hairy can help reduce water loss by slowing the flow of air over the surface of the leaf and increasing humidity. And, even though they are often very small, each hair casts a tiny shadow, which reduces the amount of sunlight hitting the leaf surface and lowers the temperature of the leaf. At higher altitudes or in very sunny environments the hairs also protect the leaf from damage by ultraviolet radiation. When I see a plant with very hairy grey leaves, I know that it is very likely to come from a hot, sunny, dry environment, somewhere like the Mediterranean. These visual cues are also of use to gardeners – most grey-haired plants rarely do well in shade, so give them lots of sunshine. Most of Great Britain and Ireland is not very dry, therefore relatively few of our wild plants are densely haired or grey-coloured – those we do have are largely confined to coastal areas in the south-eastern parts of these islands. Nevertheless, many of our plants do have hairs and they can be very varied in form. This variation can be key to identifying a leaf fragment.

Leaf hairs are made of plant cells. Sometimes a hair can be a single, long, thin cell or it may consist of several cells making a chain, rather like the carriages of a train. Some of these hairs are very short, less than a fraction of a millimetre long, sometimes they can be several millimetres long. Even within these so called 'simple' hairs there is further variation. Some may have enlarged bulbous bases; others have globular, glandular cells at their tip that may contain volatile oils. These glandular hairs are typically very common in members of the mint family (*Lamiaceae*), one of the larger plant families in the world, with about 7,500 species. In Britain and Ireland, there are about 80 wild species and hundreds of cultivated varieties in gardens. The aromatic, volatile oils found at the end of glandular hairs are what give members of the mint family, such as thyme, rosemary, basil and sage, their distinctive smell and taste. They also ward off certain grazing animals and reduce water loss.

Perhaps the most distinctive hairs found on plants in these islands are those that branch. Branched hairs can be very diverse in form. Some members of the daisy family (*Asteraceae*) have branched hairs that divide in two and look rather like tiny tuning forks. To the uninitiated, some of these plants with tuning-fork hairs look very similar to dandelions (*Taraxacum*). Among other features, leaf hairs are what botanists use to distinguish the tuning-fork-hair-bearing hawkbits (*Leontodon*) from dandelions. Hawkbits are examples of fairly common and widespread plants that have rather specific habitat requirements. They are unable to cope with grassland that is too dense or full of nutrients. You are unlikely to find them on new lawns or football pitches, but you are likely to see them growing on dryish, free-draining soils with a wide range of other plant species. Finding the hairs of hawkbit in a sample would certainly help me localise the kind of environment the sample came from. Sadly, dandelions are not so helpful. As things stand, we know of nearly 250 species of dandelion in Britain and Ireland. Many of these are widespread and common, while others are very rare and restricted to specialised habitats such as mountain tops or ancient fens. The trouble is, they are rather hard to identify at the best of times. Undamaged mature leaves, flowers, pollen and seed need to be examined; they are almost impossible to identify from a leaf fragment. So far, I have not thought of a way in which I can use dandelions in forensic casework.

Some of the most beautiful hairs are also some of the most distinctive. Many of our wild plants have variations on a star-shaped pattern; these branched stellate hairs often look like thin-limbed octopuses or starfish. They also have the advantage that they tend to break off easily and can become attached to clothing, carpet or hair, and so have the potential to be very useful in forensic work. Some members of the cabbage (*Brassicaceae*) and mallow (*Malvaceae*) families have very distinctive stellate hairs, as do ivy and the invasive non-native buddleia.

Presenting scientific information is not always easy. I need to be able to present my observations verbally in a way that aids an active investigation. Dazzling a CSM with my knowledge of *Peronosporomycotos* (my PhD subject) is not going to help. Retaining scientific rigour whilst being accessible to the non-expert can be challenging. Writing reports, both for the police and for the courts is a slow and, at times, tedious job. Each word needs to be carefully considered and every piece of information carefully checked. The slightest mistake is just what barristers are looking for to demolish you in court. A thoughtfully worded report is an important step in ensuring that all my observations and actions are clearly presented. It is also important that the information and reasoning behind my conclusions are evident. Apparently minor errors in referencing of information such as dates, times or exhibit numbers are potentially catastrophic – they are just the sort of lapse that a barrister needs to cast doubt on the credibility of an expert witness. A poorly written report is very likely to result in a court appearance that will be a very unpleasant experience. Having said that, a scientifically robust and well written report does not guarantee an expert will be spared a grilling. If there is something that is contentious or needs examining, the expert witness will be called. To date, I've submitted quite a few reports, but I have only been called to court three times.

Waiting to be called to give evidence can be both tedious and anxiety-inducing. My mind races through the report, hunting for errors and panicking when I think I have found some. I have an encrypted hard drive that I keep my forensic casework on, and this will come out so that I can read past emails and check images for overlooked information. Luckily, we're rarely alone as expert witnesses. There will usually be several of us, each undertaking our own tension-management regimes. We all end up with the demeanours of teenagers cramming for an exam; some of us flashing our confidence, others taming their fears. At the last court case I attended, there were five of us waiting to give evidence, each with our own specialisms. Alongside me was a biological statistician, a gunshot residue expert, someone who analysed shatter fragments patterns in glass, and another who worked on DNA. That's a lot of scientific information for a jury to understand in one day.

Even though an expert witness may be engaged by either the prosecution or the defence, the primary duty of expert witnesses is to the court. In other words, we must aim to present our evidence and conclusions in an unbiased manner. I and other expert witnesses are required to comply with what are called *The Criminal Procedures Rules*. These rules govern what the duties of an expert witness are and how to conduct our work. I have also undergone extensive background and security checks; these are reviewed on a regular basis to ensure that I am still of good character! This fact usually results in mirth from my family and friends who invariably think that my character is certainly open to question.

Archives and data sources are essential when doing any form of research, and this is certainly true when examining evidence. I would dearly love to have a digital photographic archive of the fruits and hairs of plants found growing in the wild and in our gardens. It would be very handy and save a lot of time. Unfortunately, no digital archive currently exists in the United Kingdom and is unlikely to in the current economic climate. In the meantime, I continue to verify my plant fragment identities the traditional way, using an herbarium.

Herbariums are the single most valuable resource for my work. My quick and dirty explanation for them is that they are essentially plant libraries. But that does not fully do justice to them. Libraries are wondrous places but, in the main, they contain copies of material that can be found elsewhere. Each item in an herbarium, however, is unique. An herbarium is a collection of pressed, dried plants. In previous centuries they were mounted in bound volumes and called *hortus siccus*, which means 'dried garden'. Today, each specimen is mounted on an individual sheet. Each sheet has information on where, when and by whom it was collected, as well as the plant's scientific name. Hopefully, it will also have a unique identification number; the reason herbarium sheets have these is that there are about 350 million specimens in the world's herbariums. It's incredibly easy to mislay a sheet, and having a unique number helps curators keep track, especially as many institutes loan them to other organisations for research purposes.

The Natural History Museum's herbarium is estimated to contain 5.2 million individual sheets. While I worked at the museum, I looked after about 620,000 specimens collected from Britain and Ireland, which of course is a lot more than the estimated 4,800 species found growing wild on these islands. Unlike Noah, museum curators are not content with two representatives of each species, we like lots. The main reason for this is that species vary, often a great deal. Plants are especially variable and having a reference collection to examine to is very useful in understanding natural variation within a plant species. This variation is caused by a huge range of factors relating to the species' evolutionary history. In some cases, herbariums can hold hundreds or even thousands of specimens from each species. The scale of the museum's collections is driven by one of its key roles – to protect and conserve the scientific and cultural heritage of natural history specimens. If the collections are of value and the museum has the resources (an increasingly doubtful question these days), then they will be taken in. This plenitude of specimens is incredibly useful for an ever-widening range of scientific uses, including climate-change research. Museum specimens contain locked-in past environmental information about how our world is changing. They are also invaluable for forensics.

I once received a request to examine some material in an arson case. The suspect was arrested on suspicion of attempting to burn down a building. Having made the attempt, the suspect made their getaway. Unfortunately for them, about ten minutes later they were stopped by a police officer who was aware of the incident. The officer decided the person was behaving suspiciously and arrested them. They were taken to a police station where the officer did something unusual (or as far as I am aware, it's unusual). The suspect was made to stand on plastic sheeting and their clothing was careful examined and brushed down. The debris that fell to the floor, as well as that retrieved from the suspect's clothing, was retained as an exhibit and sent to me. The amount recovered was tiny, two leaves and one flower, each no more than 5 millimetres long.

The police also visited the crime scene and retrieved another exhibit; some dried vegetation pulled from the property's fencing that had been used to start the fire and this too was sent to me. Each exhibit was sent in separate sealed bags. Because the plant fragments retrieved from the suspect were so tiny, I examined them under a dissecting microscope and quickly confirmed that they were a match and from the same type of plant. The leaves were small, needle-shaped and their margins were slightly folded back on themselves, with lots of glands all over their surface. This is an unusual form for plants growing wild in Britain and straight away led me to suspect that the plant originally came from a warmer part of the world with an arid or Mediterranean climate. The flowers were also distinctive and did not resemble any widespread British wild plant. After some musing, I had a reasonable idea what the plant was and which part of the world it originally came from.

I was in a rush. It's fair to say I was always in a rush. People have the idea that the life of museum curators is sedate. Not so. Most curators are expert at multitasking, and typically we have several curation projects and groups of volunteers on the go at any one time. I'd also be attempting to write or contribute to papers, draft grant applications, answer email enquiries from all over the world, contribute to the latest gallery development, attend fundraising jamborees with billionaires and do the odd interview for the television. Lots of fun, most of the time!

The impending sense of rush-related sweaty palms was exacerbated by the fact that I knew I had to leave the comfort of my relatively small collection of 620,000 specimens and head into the Natural History Museum's General Herbarium which runs to several million. The General Herbarium covers the whole world minus Britain and Ireland. It's an amazing collection. Highlights in the museum's botany collections include the first set of plant specimens collected from Australia by Sir Joseph Banks and Daniel Solander when they accompanied Captain James Cook on his voyage to Australia in 1768 and the plants that Carl Linnaeus, the 'father of taxonomy', studied in his youth in Holland.

The herbarium is cavernous and, even after being at the museum for so long, I still had moments when I couldn't remember where things were. I needed to get an answer to the police as soon as possible, and so I pounced on a retired colleague who continued to work voluntarily on the collections. She also had a labyrinthine knowledge of the herbarium. The Natural History Museum's collection enchant many and it is not unusual for retirees to continue their labours, sometimes for decades. I asked my colleague to do me a favour and see if she could track down a specimen that matched the exhibits I was working on. About 45 minutes later she was at my desk with a match (about two or three hours faster than I expected the task to take). She was carefully holding a specimen in front of her (there are stringent rules on the handling of specimens; 300-year-old dead dried plants can easily be ruined). One glance told me that she'd got it – I knew she would, she's brilliant but self-deprecating. My retired colleague does not have a doctorate and hails from an era when the museum was very hierarchical, those with qualifications were considered superior.

To be absolutely certain, I examined the museum specimen under the microscope. It was certainly the same plant, or very closely related. I noted down the collection details and returned the specimen to its place in the herbarium. Then, I returned to my desk to do a little research on the plant. It is not a plant that would be found wild in Britain. The plant hailed from the drier parts of South East Asia and Australia; it is occasionally grown here in botanic gardens but not outside, because it's too cold in most places here. Further searching led me to learn that it is sometimes used to make brooms and light brushwood fencing. The last piece of information is very satisfying. The exhibit seized at the building originated from brushwood fencing. I wrote up my observations and my conclusion, which was that the most likely source of the leaf and flower fragments taken from the suspects clothing was from the crime scene.

Every one of us who uses environmental information in forensics is either directly or indirectly dependent upon the millions of specimens and collections housed in our natural history collections. Profiling soil types is dependent upon the knowledge accrued by several centuries of soil scientists examining and collecting soil samples from all over the country. These archives of soils are essential tools for understanding the diversity of soils we have and where they originate from. Searching the Soilscapes map of the Cranfield Soil and AgriFood Institute, I learn that the soil from my mother's village is 'Soilscape 7: Freely draining slightly acid but base-rich soils' and that this soil type covers 3.1 per cent of England and Wales. Other resources like the UK Soil Observatory provide more detailed technical information. Using information resources such as these, an investigator can examine soil collected from the possessions of a suspect and provide important evidence about where they have been.

After my first ever crime scene, my entomology colleagues at the museum carefully examined the larval and pupal samples I collected. The larvae and pupae were most likely compared to the collections amassed during their decades of working in entomology and forensics. Much of their work involves understanding how fast insect larvae develop. Insect larvae feeding on bodies, or pupae found nearby can be used as a means of estimating the post-mortem interval – basically, how long someone has been dead. Using pig carcasses, they did dozens of research experiments looking at how the insects develop under different environmental conditions. Ideally, all research should be published as a paper in a peer-reviewed journal. Peer review is the process of checking that the work has been undertaken thoroughly and that the paper's conclusions accurately reflect the observations. To support their work, scientists such as my entomology colleagues will keep voucher specimens collected during the study. These will then have been stored alongside the other 80 million or so specimens that the Natural History Museum looks after. The preserved museum specimens are an essential part of the information supporting the published scientific work.

Seeds and fruit are another type of plant material often isolated from exhibits seized at a crime scene or from a suspect. Like hairs, seeds and fruit are very variable. Many are usually readily identifiable if they are not too badly damaged. What is the difference between a seed and a fruit? Botanically speaking, a fruit is the structure that bears the seed or seeds.

It is not the same as the culinary use of the word; to us botanists, fruit can either be hard or soft, dry or succulent, edible or poisonous. Fruit structure is immensely variable. The main reason for this is that the fruit of many plants play a key role in the dispersal of the seed into the environment, which is vital for a plant's survival. Like young humans, plants need to get away from the parents.

Some fruit types may be of limited value in the forensic environment. Those that are dispersed by the wind, such as the fruits of birch or maples and sycamore (*Acer* spp.), are highly mobile and may be found a considerable distance from their parent plant. Some of the most useful are those that are only dispersed a short distance or have evolved to be spread by animals. Many wild plants have fruit that have evolved to catch onto the fur or feathers of passing animals and birds. These often attach to the clothing of suspects or victims. Plants such as burdock (*Arctium*), goosegrass or cleavers (*Galium aparine*), and wood avens are examples of common plants that are often attached to our clothing after a walk in the woods. Plants such as this are very good at linking a suspect to a specific type of habitat. Even when found in soil samples, the remains of seeds and pieces of plant tissue can be very helpful in determining what sort of habitat the suspect has been in. The wild plant communities found growing on the margins of arable fields are very different from those growing in permanent grassland. Differences such as these can potentially help a botanist confirm where a crime took place or link a suspect to a crime scene or a victim. Knowing the identity of plants, understanding where they grow and how they reproduce is key to being able to do this.

11
The Curious Microscopic World

Fear of dying is embedded within all of us. Some of us learn to find ways to manage that fear. Sadly, others are haunted by it. For many people, the way of dying that most frightens them is drowning. When I was around eight years old, one of my friends nearly drowned in our local village pond. We were mucking around on the ice and she fell through. I can still clearly see her face peering up at us through the ice. We were paralysed with fear and fascination. Luckily, she pulled herself back to the hole she had fallen through, and we were able to help her climb out.

I have read a few accounts of near drownings and many of them describe the panic and the pain. I can relate to this. Oxygen deprivation hurts. Like many people, I have asthma. A bad asthma attack is really painful. Homicide by drowning appears to be rare and is usually only accomplished if the assailant is more powerful than their victim. Not surprisingly, people fight back if they are pushed underwater. Occasionally, a victim will be drugged or knocked unconscious before being placed in the water.

Rather surprisingly, there are several forms of drowning. 'Dry' downing occurs when, after being submerged, the person attempts to breathe but the muscles of the larynx contract and the airway is blocked. The person dies of oxygen deprivation, but no water reaches their lungs. This appears to be relatively uncommon. More frequently people die by 'wet' drowning in which water enters the lungs. In cases such as this, there is no spasm of the larynx muscles and water is free to pass down the airway into the lungs. 'Secondary' downing occurs after removal from water and may occur within half an hour or after several days. Basically, the lungs are so damaged and their ability to allow oxygen to pass into the blood stream is so impaired that the person dies. Lastly, some people die owing to 'immersion syndrome'. In cases such as this the heart stops because of a neurological shock. This sometimes occurs when people dive into still, deep lakes that have a layer of cold water beneath the uppermost warm layer. It is usually possible to determine what type of drowning the person suffered during post-mortem examination.

I am quite often asked about drownings. I don't usually work on these cases but a former colleague at the Natural History Museum does. He is a diatomist, a specialist in the biology of the group of organisms known as diatoms. These microscopic organisms can be either single celled or live in many-celled colonies. Diatoms are algae, which means they use sunlight energy but don't have complex tissues like most land plants. Algae are confusing and complex. The algae that most people are familiar with, especially the green 'pond scum', are not related to diatoms but are more closely linked to land plants. Curiously, some types of 'pond scum' are not even algae: they are flowering plants (*Lemna* spp.) and some of their closest living relatives are lords-and-ladies (*Arum* spp.) and the enormous Swiss cheese plant (*Monstera deliciosa*). On the other hand, diatoms belong to a diverse lineage of microorganisms that even many biologists have never heard of. Their nearest relative that you'll be familiar with are brown seaweeds like bladderwrack (*Fucus* spp.), the seaweeds that make popping sounds when you walk on it. There is much to marvel at about diatoms. They have been around for a long time, since at least the Triassic Period (250-200 million years ago) and are sometimes so abundant that they form their own geological feature, diatomaceous earth, which is made up of the fossilised remains of diatom skeletons. Diatomaceous earth is commercially extracted because it can be used in the filtration of swimming pools or fish tanks, as a fine mild abrasive for toothpaste and metal polishes, as an insecticide, or to make nitroglycerin more stable and prevent unwanted explosions. What makes diatoms so remarkable is silica. Unusually amongst living organisms, diatom skeletons are made of silica. In most animals, the skeleton is calcium based; in plants the equivalent to the skeleton is largely made up of cellulose or lignin. Relatively few organism groups have skeletons made of silica, and in most instances, they are microscopic; an exception are some sponges that have silica 'spicules' that act as part of their skeleton. The silica is the key to why diatoms are useful in crime-scene work.

One surprising aspect of drowning is that as a person attempts to breathe, the pressure inside the lungs is enough to push the diatom cells in the water through the lung membranes and into the blood stream. The cells then circulate around the body and finally lodge in the major organs as the blood circulation fails. The presence of diatoms in the organs is potentially good evidence of some types of drowning (but not 'dry' drowning, for example). Collecting a sample of diatoms from a body is not straightforward and this is where one of the properties of silica becomes important. Silica is tough and heat resistant, a lot more so than human tissue. During the post-mortem examination, a small piece of tissue, usually liver or bone marrow, will be removed to be sampled. The tissue is then 'ashed' by being heated sufficiently to burn the tissue but leave the silica shell of the diatoms intact. There are other means of extracting the diatoms from the tissue, for example digesting in nitric acid, but 'ashing' is the most frequently used technique in this country. The prepared ash can then be examined under a high-powered microscope. Diatom cells are fairly small, most are between 10 and 80 micrometres across. Some can be up to 200 micrometres or rarely over a millimetre. A micrometre is one thousandth of a millimetre. Only the smaller types of diatoms, those that are 60 micrometres or less, are able to pass through into the blood stream.

Diatoms are diverse. Scientists don't know how many species of diatom there are, and estimates vary between 20,000 and 2 million! Diatoms are usually restricted to either fresh or marine waters. In Britain and Ireland there are about 2,500 known species of freshwater diatom. Many of these species are widespread, while others are restricted in distribution or specialists of certain habitat types. The key to identifying diatoms is their silica. The siliceous skeleton of diatoms originates from their cell walls, which are called frustules. Not only are frustules incredibly beautiful, they are varied in shape and ornamentation. This variation is key to identifying which type of diatom is present in a sample and establishing what type of water body the diatoms originated from. The water of swimming pools or bath water will have very different diatom communities in them compared to an isolated pond in a wood or a canal. So, the presence of diatoms in a dead person's organs can help confirm that they drowned and in what type of water body this happened. The key to confirming that someone died in a particular stretch of water is getting a sample from that water body, quickly! Diatom populations are highly dynamic: small shifts in water temperature, nutrient availability or light levels will change the abundance of the diatoms and can change the species composition. If an investigating team delays sampling by even a few days, the diatom community may be very different, and any comparison is likely to be pointless. For diatom-based evidence to be of value, the retrieval of environmental samples containing diatoms should be overseen by a scientist who is experienced in working with them.

I'm a great fan of pre-Victorian scientists, because they managed to achieve incredible discoveries about our world, often with only the most basic of equipment. In the mid-17th century a Dutchman, Antonie van Leeuwenhoek, built his own microscope and documented the microscopical world of fungi, insects, plants and single-celled organisms that he called animalcules. His pioneering work revolutionised biology and was internationally applauded. In England, his work was championed by the Royal Society. Founded in 1660, the Royal Society was devoted to 'Improving Natural Knowledge'. In 1703, several decades after Leeuwenhoek's discoveries, the Royal Society published an anonymous work originating from 'a gentleman in the country'. This described for the first time a previously unknown microscopic organism, collected growing on algae 'from the shallow side of a pond' that was made up of 'many pretty branches, compos'd of rectangular oblongs and exact squares that were joyn'd together'. The gentleman was describing Tabellaria, a diatom. This unknown man's observations exemplify the curious minds of the era. They remind me that, when attending a crime scene, where possible, explore all aspects of the environment.

A few months after I started doing crime-scene work, I came across a word that fascinated me: adipocere. The sound of the word has a strange beauty that I found captivating. On learning what the word meant I was weirdly enthralled. Adipocere is also called grave wax, corpse wax or mortuary wax, though these names lack some of adipocere's charm. The phenomenon was described by the seventeenth-century polymath Sir Thomas Browne who was one of the most innovative thinkers of his age. Hailing from Norwich, he was schooled at Winchester College before studying as an undergraduate at the University of Oxford. He then studied medicine at Padua and Montpelier universities. Browne would have witnessed anatomical dissections during his time studying and probably in his later life as a physician back in Norwich. He also had a fascination for the rituals of death. In his 1658 publication Hydriotaphia, Urne Buriall, or, a Discourse of the Sepulchral Urns lately found in Norfolk, Browne described what befalls the body in the grave; he observed that 'Teeth, bones and hair, give the most lasting defiance to corruption' and that on examining a buried corpse that had been buried for ten years 'we met with a fat concretion, where the nitre of the earth, and the salt and lixivious liquor of the body, had coagulated large lumps of fat, into the consistence of the hardest castle-soap'. Browne's description exemplifies the enquiring seventeenth-century spirit, but it also vividly describes adipocere. Incidentally, castle-soap is an anglicisation of Castile soap, a soap made of olive (*Olea europaea*) and laurel (*Laurus nobilis*) oil that originated from the Middle East.

The creation of adipocere requires very specific environmental conditions, so not all graves contain it. First, there must be a lack of oxygen in the environment. We tend to think of atmospheric oxygen as being life-giving, but in too high a concentration, it kills. Some organisms require very low levels of oxygen to survive and these anaerobes, as they are called, often play an important role in decay processes. One group of anaerobic bacteria are particularly efficient at breaking down the fatty components of our bodies into alcohol and that soapy substance, adipocere.

One of the amazing properties of adipocere is its stability. Once it has formed it can persist for centuries in the right environmental conditions. This stability is the key to its value in forensics; adipocere encapsulates and preserves the finest details, including cellular details in human tissue or in some cases the last meal eaten. In the late autumn of 1911, Patrick Higgins took his two young sons, John and William, on their last walk. He tied them together and threw them into a quarry lake near Winchburgh, Scotland. Higgins was a single parent, his wife having died in 1910, and he had been sleeping rough in a brickworks where he was working as a labourer. He had sought help in supporting the children but to no avail, and shortly before the murder, he had been imprisoned for two months for neglecting the boys. After the boys' disappearance, Higgins claimed that they were in the care of others. Some 18 months later, the boys' bodies floated to the lake surface and their father was arrested and charged with their murder. Despite his plea of mental incapacity, he was found guilty of murder and executed on the 3rd October 1913. Before the trial, the bodies of the boys were examined. Most of the fats in their bodies had been converted to adipocere. The adipocere preserved a great deal of their remains, including their last meal. Appallingly, the police surgeon, Sir Harvey Littlejohn, and the pathologist Sir Sydney Smith, conspired to illicitly remove some of the boys' body parts which were then taken to the University of Edinburgh. They remained in the university until very recently when a relative, Maureen Marella, requested that the boys' remains be cremated and a memorial service held. I have not had the opportunity to work with adipocere, but I suspect it could be fascinating. It is quite likely that it is a potential medium for preserving a wide range of trace evidence such as diatoms, pollen, fungal spores and fragments of vegetation on clothing as well as within the digestive tract. Most of this trace evidence would otherwise be lost during the processes of decay.

Like diatoms and pollen, the spores of fungi can be used to link a suspect to a crime scene or a victim. To most people, the word fungus conjures up mental images of either mushrooms and toadstools or mouldy bread. But the world of fungi is far more exciting than that. Earlier, I mentioned there are lots of species of plant on the planet – around 320,000 is the most recent estimate. This large number is dwarfed by the number of fungi, the most widely accepted estimate is 1.5 million species, although many scientists believe this to be on the low side. Not only are there a lot of them, many of them are localised and very specific about where they like to live. One of Europe's most fascinating fungi is the nail fungus (*Poronia punctata*). The nail fungus is so called because the fruiting body looks rather like a small old-fashioned, flat-headed nail with little dark dots on the surface of the head. Not only is it a curious-looking fungus, it also has curious habits: it lives on horse poo. Only horse poo, nothing else will do. Nail fungus is now rare, partly because the modern antibiotic medicines we give to horses kill it. This aptitude for colonising and exploiting all sorts of unusual habitats make fungi potentially very useful for forensics. However, we have a big hurdle to leap. Compared to plants or animals, we still know very little about them. The vast majority of them are microscopic and their reproductive structures, the spores, are incredibly variable. Improving our grasp of the variability and occurrence of fungal spores could add to our environmental forensics toolkit.

There have been a few cases where fungal spores, alongside pollen, have proved significant. One such case involved a young woman who was raped by her partner. Although they had consensual sexual activity earlier in the day, the sexual contact later in the day was not, and she reported him to the police. Because of the earlier contact, it was not possible to use human DNA evidence, therefore environmental evidence was needed to corroborate the victim's account. The suspect maintained that they had consensual sex in an open area of parkland, while his accuser said he had assaulted her in woodland. Detailed sampling of both locations and the clothing of both the victim and the suspect produced pollen and fungal spore types that corroborated the victim's account. The fungal spores from the woodland were particularly distinctive and strongly supported the proposition that both the victim and the suspect had been in woodland. On being presented

12
The Case of the Scabby Ankle

Crime affects us all. It deprives some of us of loved ones and it leaves some of us poorer or with ruined homes and lives. It affects everyone's tax bill. And it is not just humans that suffer the effects of criminality. Internationally, wildlife crime is a major concern, and in some cases is on a par with arms-smuggling, people-trafficking and the drugs trade in the harm it does to societies. The illegal and unsustainable trade in animals like pangolins, rhinoceroses, elephants and tigers is a major contributing factor towards these animals being driven to extinction. This trade is sufficiently serious that it now regularly hits the headlines. Plants are also being extirpated by illegal trafficking, yet this rarely makes the papers and campaigns to protect them don't garner the support of royalty.

When I was a student at Kew Gardens, an illegal shipment of cacti was seized at a major UK airport. The plants were sent to Kew for identification and care prior to the court case being held; this is another example of the services that botanical gardens provide to society. Many cacti are increasingly at risk of extinction owing to their popularity in horticulture. People who illegally harvest wild cacti are rather romantically described as cactus rustlers, though there is nothing romantic in their actions. They are robbing the Americas (where all but one of the world's cacti species originate from) of its biological treasures. One of the seized cacti sent to Kew had been ripped out of the ground by a truck, using a rope tied around the cactus. The cactus had half-moon shaped cuts in its stem where the rope had dug into it. Luckily, the plant survived and was ultimately incorporated into Kew's Living Collections. Every time I return to Kew, I pop into the Princess of Wales Conservatory to wish it well. It's quite close to the path, so see if you can spot it – the damage is still visible.

Forensic science is increasingly being deployed to combat this trade and other illegal activities directed towards wildlife. Orchids are particularly vulnerable to our depredation. Like cacti, many orchids are widely traded legally, but there is also an extensive illegal trade in live plants stolen from the wild for the lucrative and very large international black market. They are also often found in various traditional medicines and foods. As populations rise and demand increases, formerly sustainable, traditional harvesting has turned into widespread exploitation. The problem is sufficiently severe that many countries have specially trained police specialists fighting wildlife crime. In the United Kingdom, the National Wildlife Crime Unit was set up to combat cruel and criminal acts such as the persecution of birds of prey (raptors), hare coursing, badger baiting and fox hunting. People illegally collecting and trading in stuffed wild birds (especially raptors), bird eggs, butterflies and wild orchids are also significant targets for investigators. Much of this work is undertaken using various surveillance techniques, as well as newer approaches involving non-human DNA and hair- and feather -follicle identification (the hairs and feathers of many animal species can be identified using microscopy and comparison with museum collections).

Forensic laboratories investigating wildlife crime increasingly use DNA-based tools to identify processed or powdered materials derived from some of the planet's rarest and most endangered organisms such as rhinoceros horns or dried orchids. Several years ago, I visited Yunnan in southern China to film a documentary for Discovery Channel on China's amazingly diverse plant life and how the people of China are still, despite globalisation and modernisation, dependent upon this bounty. One of the segments we filmed was about the developing horticultural industry growing orchid species for traditional Chinese medicine (TCM). One of the most important plants in TCM and one of the nine 'magical herbs' is an orchid, *Dendrobium officinale*, which is known as Tie Pi Shi Hu (铁皮石斛, iron skin dendrobium) to the Chinese. This plant has been harvested from the wild for hundreds of years and is now sadly at risk of extinction as a wild plant. The Chinese are trying to meet the burgeoning domestic and international demand for this plant by cultivating it, but wild -collected plants are still sold for a premium. One of the ways that trade can be regulated is through laboratory testing. These laboratories depend upon museum and botanic garden collections to provide valuable resources for comparison and to validate identifications of seized goods.

Not only do biological collections hold valuable material for fighting wildlife crime, they are repositories of information that can help us understand the emergence of new diseases. In 2009, some of the first cases of what became known as seasonal canine illness were identified on the Queen's estate at Sandringham and at other locations across the country. The illness caused some dogs that had been walked in woodland to start vomiting and to have diarrhoea. In severe cases and without veterinary intervention, the dogs died. Not surprisingly, the unexpected and rapid arrival of this illness across the country caused widespread concern among dog owners.

Researchers at the Animal Heath Trust led the efforts to discover what was the source of this mysterious and distressing illness. A wide range of causes were suggested, including agricultural chemicals, rodenticides or illegally placed chemicals used to kill birds of prey. There were also suggestions that the cause might be botanical. One popular suggested cause was blue-green algae. These are fascinating organisms that are more closely related to bacteria than to other types of algae or land plants. They are found in an incredibly wide range of environments around the planet and are ecologically very important. Some blue-green algae, or *Cyanobacteria* as they are collectively known to scientists, commonly form part of the symbiotic union with fungi that we call lichen. The beautiful hues of orange, brown, green and grey lichen that adorn our trees, rocks and buildings would not exist without them. Some blue-green algae also have a reputation for causing poisonings of either humans or animals. These poisonings normally occur after contact and ingestion of inland waters polluted by agricultural fertiliser or animal-waste run-off. The excess nutrients cause algal blooms, meaning that some blue-green algae populations proliferate and thrive, sometimes to environmentally hazardous levels, in the nutrient-laden water.

By 2011, the number of seasonal canine illness cases had gradually increased, and concern grew. Early that September, I joined Animal Health Trust researchers at the Sandringham estate to investigate the possibility that there was a botanical cause. We met a couple who, just a few days earlier, had gone for a walk in the woods with their dogs. Shortly afterwards one of the dogs rapidly became ill and died. I spent the day dashing in and out of the bushes looking for clues, but I was unable to see anything that could have caused the dogs to sicken and die. I looked for likely sources of toxic blue-green algae but found none. I also scouted for toxic fungi and plants. While the wood did have some of these, such as foxglove (*Digitalis purpurea*) and cherry laurel (*Prunus laurocerasus*), all the plants and fungi I saw had been present for many decades. If they had been the cause, the illness would have been noticed decades earlier. We had drawn a blank. I must admit, from what the Animal Health Trust researchers had told me beforehand, I was not expecting to find a botanical cause. I suspected a virus or an insect.

On my way back to London, I felt a little itch around my ankles, and by the time I got to bed it was becoming bothersome. When I woke up the next morning my ankles had ballooned and were bright red. I headed straight to the doctor and described what had happened. We both suspected that it might have been caused by some unseen critter. My doctor prescribed some anti-histamines, and by the end of the day the swelling had gone down significantly, but my ankles still looked awful. I took a photograph of them and consulted one of my colleagues at the Natural History Museum who is an acarologist, an expert on mites.

Mites belong to the same evolutionary group as spiders. Many of them are plant pests but some cause illnesses in animals. These mites are known either as harvest mites or chiggers and are largely confined to the warmer parts of the world. Worldwide, some harvest-mite species transmit some rather nasty disease-causing organism, such as the bacteria that is the cause of scrub typhus. My colleague agreed that my symptoms were consistent with harvest mites. It seemed likely that I had picked up my unwanted guests while I was rummaging in the undergrowth. However, none of the species found in Great Britain were known to cause such symptoms. Is it possible that there is a new harvest-mite species or a disease-causing organism that is vectored by them here in the UK? This is a plausible explanation; biologists have documented large-scale migrations of plants and animals due to environmental change over the last few decades. We also know that international trade via shipping and aircraft is an important 'pathway' (as it's described in policy-speak) for biological invasions. To date, we remain unsure, but harvest mites have been observed on dogs suffering from seasonal canine illness and they appear to be the strongest contender as the causal agent.

The following autumn, the museum was contacted by a producer from the BBCs *Countryfile* television programme. Would I do an interview alongside the Animal Health Trust describing our investigations? I agreed and a few days later I met *Countryfile* presenter Tom Heap at Sandringham to do the interview. I was prepared and relaxed; one of the skills that my time at the museum taught me was media work. My first contact with *Countryfile* had been with one of my childhood heroes, John Craven. He interviewed me about a research and citizen science project on bluebells that I had been working on. We met in a wood in south London. Unfortunately, it hammered down with rain all day and we both had awful colds. I remember sitting in the car with him, glumly wishing the day would just end and I'm sure he felt the same way too. Nevertheless, I was a little star-struck. Luckily, the weather on the day of the interview with Tom was much better and all went well. We spent several hours retracing our earlier step through the Sandringham estate (this time I avoided clambering through the undergrowth) while being filmed by the BBC crew. Foolishly, I mentioned the picture of my mite-ravaged ankles. The team were very keen to have a copy for the programme and several weeks later, my scabby ankles appeared on the programme I'm quietly optimistic that one day they may prove to have saved the life of someone's dog.

As well as hunting for poisonous plants and fungi in our landscape, I have also grown quite a few. In my teens, I had a flowerbed devoted to poisonous plants: monk's-hood (*Aconitum napellus*), hemlock water-dropwort (*Oenanthe crocata*) and oleander (*Nerium oleander*) were favourites. My mum and I used to happily muse on the lethal dose required to despatch my father, who had long since removed himself from our lives. It's fair to say that my family can be quite dark sometimes.

I have worked on one or two cases involving poisonous plants and fatalities but, for me, they are rare. This rarity is probably due to several reasons. First, many potential poisoners would have no idea what plants were poisonous and how to find or identify them. So, in most cases, poisoners (or people attempting to commit suicide) tend to reach for the medicine cabinet or the chemicals in the garage or the garden shed. Secondly, most unrefined plant toxins are relatively inefficient and slow working compared to what can be found in a bottle on a shelf. It can take quite a long time to die from some of the toxins present in plants or fungi found in the UK, and there is always a risk that the victim will vomit them up. Finally, there is quite a high chance that the victim will recover from poisoning by most plant toxins if they are treated in time.

Generally, there are adequate treatments for most toxic plants and fungi found in these islands. There are exceptions, one of which is the deathcap (*Amanita phalloides*). The inherent danger of this fungus is rather given away by its name. You stand a very high chance of dying if you consume enough of this fungus, even with modern treatments. One of the reasons that deathcap is so awful is that the most toxic compounds, of which the amatoxin α amanitin is the most powerful, are thermostable – cooking does not break the molecule down and it remains active. Apparently, deathcap tastes quite nice, so you're unlikely to spit it out while eating it. Unfortunately, by the time symptoms develop, typically about twelve hours after ingestion, the person is already in trouble. It can take several days to die of deathcap poisoning, and as the toxins work their way through the body the victim may appear to be recovering only to finally be felled by the constant onslaught of the almost indestructible α amanitin.

Thankfully, poisoning by deathcap is very uncommon. However, each autumn one of my mycological friends is on standby awaiting calls from hospitals relating to accidental poisoning by various fungi. The lucky chap on occasion receives stomach contents couriered to him in the depths of the night. He then needs to sort through the goo and examine the fragments under a microscope to identify the fungus. While I've not had to sit waiting for the courier at two in the morning, I have received samples of stomach contents from recently deceased people. My role is simply to identify the plant fragments. I can go no further than that, because I'm not a toxicologist and have no medical training. My observations will be passed on to someone more suitably qualified who will ascertain whether the plant material I have identified was the cause of death.

The natural world is a powerhouse of toxicity. The botulinum protein derived from the bacteria *Clostridium botulinum* is the most acutely lethal known toxin, and the deathcap and its charmingly named relative the destroying angel (*Amanita virosa*) live up to their names. There are many poisonous plants in our landscape and gardens, but most are totally safe to handle. The castor-oil plant (*Ricinus communis*), a commonly grown summer bedding plant and source of castor oil, is also the source of one of the most notorious toxins known to man, ricin. The Bulgarian dissident writer Georgi Markov was assassinated by an agent of the Bulgarian Secret Service using ricin. Markov was waiting for a bus near Waterloo Bridge in London when he felt a sharp sting in his right thigh. As he turned around, he saw a man picking up an umbrella, who then proceeded to hurry away. Markov died four days later in hospital. A post-mortem examination of his body revealed a small metal pellet, less than two millimetres across, in his thigh. The pellet, which had tiny holes drilled into it, had been filled with ricin.

About ten years ago I was extremely lucky to be invited to the Black Museum at New Scotland Yard. It is one of the most extraordinary places on the planet, full of exhibits and memorabilia originating from some of the most notorious crimes in our recent history. Among the profusion of ropes, guns, cleavers and other ghastly instruments of death, sits the tiny silvery coloured platinum and iridium pellet that killed Markov. It looks almost gem-like on its mount.

The museum is full of incredible and often very disturbing objects. One of the most captivating objects is the top of the skull of a man murdered by his former lover. As I remember it, at some point towards the end of the 19th century, the young heir to a wealthy family fell for a maid in the family household. Their relationship was discovered by the man's family and the maid was expelled from the house, pregnant. Sadly, owing to her poverty and pregnancy, she had no option but to resort to prostitution to survive. Many years later she had established herself in her new profession when she received a fresh client. It was her former lover and, appallingly, he failed to recognise her. Engulfed with rage and a desire for revenge, she arranged for him to be murdered next time he visited. After the deed was done, she and her accomplice decapitated him and had his skull mounted in silver and fashioned into a goblet. For years after, at the end of each long working day, she would pour red wine into his skull and drink to her vicious victory.

One of my early childhood memories was of my mother placing a pile of tomatoes on the table and telling me that my father had collected them from the nearby sewage works. I was fascinated by the idea that the seed had travelled through someone's insides and had subsequently germinated. I don't remember feeling any aversion to the idea of eating something that had originated in this manner. In hindsight, it probably indicated that I was cut out for this job. Exploration of stomach contents is not only an important tool when assessing the probability of poisoning. Stomach and intestinal tract contents can also be very useful in identifying the last meal a person consumed and estimating how long someone has been dead (the post-mortem interval). In the United States, two researchers, Jane Bock and David Norris, have undertaken pioneering work examining and identifying plant fragments found in the digestive tracts of the deceased.

Certain plant tissue types are very tough and can withstand the grinding of our teeth, the acids in our stomachs and the enzymes that permeate our digestive tract. Many are so tough that they come out the other end partially or fully intact. On top of this durability, many of these plant tissues have distinctive morphological features that allow some vegetable components of the deceased's last meal to be identified. It is possible to identify commonly eaten food such as potatoes, beans, cabbages and tomatoes from their mashed-up remains.

The infamous murder of 'Adam', a young boy whose mutilated torso was discovered in the River Thames in London on 21 September 2001 is largely remembered because of the very strong evidence linking his death to a ritualistic killing known as muti. Adam has never been identified, but his DNA and the mineral composition of his bones strongly suggested that he originated from near Benin City in Nigeria. This knowledge about Adam's origins was vital. Careful examination of Adam's stomach contents revealed that, shortly before his death, he had been given a meal containing 19 plant species, including beans. The remains of the beans from Adam's digestive tract were identified by examining the outer shell, or testa, as it's known botanically. In many plant families, the arrangement of the cells on the surface of the testa is very distinctive and can be used to identify the plant consumed. In Adam's case, the testae were identified by a plant anatomist from the Royal Botanic Gardens in Kew as originating from the Calabar or ordeal bean (*Physostigma venenosum*). The work at Kew would have been greatly hampered if the police had not known of Adam's origins. Worldwide, there are thousands of members of the pea and bean family (*Fabaceae*), searching the whole of the planet's legume diversity would take a lot longer than focussing on one specific region.

The Calabar bean originates from tropical Africa and has long been associated with traditional beliefs, including the identification by ordeal of people believed to be witches. Suspected witches were forced to drink a concoction made of the bean and if they died, they were considered guilty; if they lived, they were deemed innocent. The police believe Adam was given Calabar bean as a means of immobilising him prior to his throat being cut. His head and limbs were then cut off. The active ingredient in Calabar bean is physostigmine, which affects the neural signalling to the muscles, resulting in seizures, salivation, loss of bladder and bowel control and, with a large enough dose, death by asphyxiation or cardiac arrest. Despite its fearful reputation, links with witchcraft and Adam's tragic death, therapeutic doses of physostigmine have been used to treat glaucoma and as an antidote for poisoning by deadly nightshade (*Atropa belladonna*) and thorn-apple (*Datura stramonium*). Curiously, Adam had also been fed with thorn-apple, a plant with a fearsome reputation for its toxic and hallucinogenic properties. The thorn-apple belongs to a plant family that has regularly played a part in poisonings – the tomato family, *Solanaceae*. *Solanaceae* is full of very toxic species, including deadly nightshade, tobacco (*Nicotiana tabacum*) and mandrake (*Mandragora officinarum*). There are also a host of economically important edible plants in the family – tomato (*Solanum lycopersicum*), potato (*S. tuberosum*) and sweet pepper (*S. annuum*) are some of the most well-known.

Tragically, Adam's killers have never been brought to justice but there is always a chance that they may. At that point, the thorough work of the forensic specialists such as the researcher at Kew may play a central role in their conviction. There is also the possibility that new techniques that were not available at the time of the investigation may help find his killers and secure their conviction.

13
The Future of
Environmental Forensics

After more than a decade of austerity, it is fair to say that policing and crime-scene examination in this country face challenging times. Public-spending cuts have had a very significant impact upon resources and, in my experience, have led to an increased unwillingness of the police to commit to specialist forensic services. It also appears immensely difficult for forces to provide training for their staff on specialist fields such as forensic botany. Without this training it is very hard to see how a crime scene manager, PolSA or a detective would consider using techniques which, in many cases, they may not have an understanding of, or may never have heard of. As police forces find it harder to fund specialist forensic examinations there is a knock-on effect; without revenue from police forces, forensic service providers are less able to provide some specialist services. Over the last few years we have seen increasing concern about the viability of the private forensics sector in this country. Some companies have folded, and I suspect others may follow.

Our society has enormous expectations of our public services. The police are expected to behave to the highest standards, and rightly so. But it's become clear to me that we also have some ludicrous expectations about how they should work. I've been horrified over the last few years to see the police being attacked in the tabloids and on social media for the temerity of taking breaks and eating while on duty. This sort of criticism is dehumanising and is born of entirely unrealistic and unachievable demands. Having spent hours crawling around on my hands and knees in the freezing cold with police staff, I have come to appreciate that, in the round, they deserve our praise. Clearly, corruption or poor procedures need to be challenged and dealt with, and, of course there are some bad apples. These are issues that are present in many of our national institutions and larger organisations. It is also apparent that there are institutional failings within our police forces that affect parts of our society disproportionately. However, I suspect that many failings are due to the underfunding of our police services. Over the last decade I've witnessed the efforts that people put into solving serious crimes and the increasingly tough constraints placed upon them to get the job done. The role that a specialist such as myself plays is relatively small, but I fear it may get smaller if we continue down the route we are taking. The police appear less prepared to commit valuable resources to explore avenues of investigation that they may be unfamiliar with, and while recent technological advances offer new ways of investigating crime, I am concerned that as investigators become more pressed for time, they will have fewer opportunities to explore these approaches.

One of the great challenges of working with the police is persuading them that an integrated approach to exploring the environment will yield the best results. Most areas of crime-scene specialist work are very much discrete entities. For example, the presence of gunshot residue is not dependent upon other forms of trace evidence such as glass fragments or fibres. This is very different to information gathered from the natural environment. Soil types can be strongly indicative of what plant communities are present, which in turn may predict what invertebrate, fungal and microbial assemblages are present.

The common rock-rose (*Helianthemum nummularium*) is a popular garden plant that tolerates a wide range of soils. In the wild, this relatively widespread plant is much fussier. Nearly all of its British and Irish locations are on calcareous soils over either limestone or chalk, except in some parts of Scotland where it is known to grow on acid soils, but even on these it's still pernickety, as it will only thrive in sunny locations and on grassland that is many decades or centuries old. The common rock-rose also has a suite of other organisms in tow, some of which are entirely dependent upon the plant. In and around the roots lives a diverse community of fungi, including species of bolete, milkcap, webcap and fibrecap. Both the rock-rose and the fungi in these mycorrhizal associations, as they are known, benefit by exchanging food and nutrients. Feeding on the unopened flower buds and pollen is the specialist pollen beetle *Meligethes solidus*. Foraging on the leaves are four species of bug, one of which, *Emelyanoviana contraria*, is extremely rare and restricted to limestone pavement in Yorkshire. Limestone pavement is not street paving, it is a scarce natural habitat created by the erosional power of water. The larvae of several species of moth, including a leaf-miner *Coleophora ochrea*, also utilise the plant. Leaf-mining insects are extraordinary: they spend much of their lives burrowing within the leaf, eating the soft tissue between the upper and lower surfaces. Also, among the leaves is the fairly widespread beetle *Mantura matthewsi*, while the much rarer *Helianthemapion aciculare* is restricted to the Great Orme in North Wales and the very rare pot beetle (*Cryptocephalus primarius*) survives in few localities in southern England. Not surprisingly, there are also a wide range of other invertebrates like the beautiful silver-studded blue butterfly (*Plebejus argus*) that feed on the plant but are not entirely dependent upon it.

While giving some insight into the complexity of our ecosystems, this example also demonstrates that biological evidence gathered as part of an investigation should not be viewed in isolation. If I were presented with an exhibit that contained heavy clay particles and rock-rose pollen, I would most likely conclude that the sample came from a garden. However, if I received a sample with chalk particles, rock-rose pollen and the wing cases of the beetle *Mantura matthewsi*, I would most likely conclude that the origin was chalk-grassland. This example may be hypothetical, but it is not far from reality. I quite often receive material that may have both soil and non-plant biological components within. While I don't consider myself professionally competent to characterise soil types or identify beetles based on their wing cases, my knowledge is sufficiently broad that I can recognise their potential evidential value in a case such as this and find someone who has the appropriate skills to identify them.

In two cases I've worked on, the need to view these biological assemblages as a whole was paramount. In one, a fellow museum biologist and I identified several very interesting organisms in an exhibit. Amazingly, there was a fragment of an extremely rare insect that is only found in one location in the whole of Britain and Ireland. This and other information led us to believe that it was extremely likely that the exhibit came from overseas. In the other case, a very violent rape and murder, the police simply refused to examine the environmental samples. In both cases, it was my view that there was a high likelihood that further scientific examination of the exhibits would reveal significant results. Frustratingly, in both cases the police refused to pursue these lines of enquiry. The last time I checked, both cases remained unsolved.

Several years later, these choices 'not to pursue' still frustrate me. It can be very hard not to get angry about decisions that you disagree with. I know this happens in all walks of life, but there is a particular sting when you are working on a murder inquiry. I don't lose sleep and I am not haunted by these decisions but they certainly irk. One of the cases is now over 6 years old and the person's family and friends continue to grieve without knowing who was responsible. I recently drove very close to where the badly decayed remains were found. As we drove, I mulled over the case and quietly cursed the decision 'not to pursue'.

Usually, I am not party as to why the police choose to discontinue an avenue of investigation. There is no obligation on their part to explain their actions to somebody such as me. They may be required to justify their actions in court, and I may be called to explain my findings and subsequent advice. The motivations of the police in these cases is unclear, but I suspect the most likely cause is lack of money. I fear that insufficient training is also a factor. The natural world is complex, it takes time and experience to understand. The police, and CSMs in particular, need training in order to be able to understand when specialist disciplines like forensic botany or entomology may be of use. I have met people who work for UK police forces who have never previously heard of forensic botany. To me, this feels like there is a need for some introductory training in all aspects of environmental forensics.

The loss of public resource has been insidious and incremental. When I was still working for the Natural History Museum, I received a request to take on the unwanted herbarium of the Forensic Science Service (FSS). The FSS was a government-owned company that provided forensic science services to police forces and government agencies of England and Wales. The FSS herbarium had been compiled by FSS staff over a period of about 30 years and was used as a reference collection. At the time of the enquiry, there was no longer anyone in the FSS who had botanical expertise, and the facility in which the collection was housed was being handed over to another organisation. Either the NHM saved the material or it would go in a skip.

Sadly, I was used to this sort of request. Very often the families of recently deceased people would find collections and want rid of them. On one occasion, I was contacted by a schoolteacher who had rescued a very fine and significant collection of several thousand specimens collected in the Victorian era. The school had no interest in the herbarium, and they were going to throw it away. Sadly, such disregard for natural history collections heritage and their historic, cultural and scientific value is not uncommon. Herbariums are merely seen as 'flower pressing' and worthless. But often they may contain significant cultural and scientific information that enrich our lives and help us understand the world around us. Even though I'd not seen the FSS collection I felt it was likely to be of scientific and historic value, so I agreed to take a look at it. Unsurprisingly, it was not in a good state. The specimens were shoved into plastic bags and clearly in need of some curatorial attention. On behalf of the trustees of the Natural History Museum, I agreed to accept the collection and accession it into the museum's holdings. Doing so would entail many hours work on the part of my team of volunteers and staff. The specimens would need to be assessed and any material that was beyond rescue would have to be discarded. The retained specimens would then be remounted on conservation grade paper (each sheet costs around 80 pence, depending on the price of paper at the time) and catalogued. Years ago, I calculated that a properly mounted and databased herbarium specimen costed about £7.50; no doubt the figure is higher now. The FSS herbarium consisted of several hundred sheets and they did not come with a cheque. The museum had to absorb the cost of saving this important material.

This happens quite a lot. Either it's saved or it goes in the bin. Rather a gun-to-the-temple situation! Luckily, my volunteers had quite a lot of fun mounting the material and were quite titillated when it came to the cannabis. I am fairly frequently called on to identify cannabis (*Cannabis sativa*). In one case the owners of a cannabis factory had attempted to destroy the plants by burning them. I'm not sure under what circumstances this happened as often I do not receive the details of the case from the police. The courier delivered a plastic container which contained the shrivelled and partially burnt remnants of foliage. They were heavily damaged and rolled up into a loose ball because of the heat. Straight away it was clear the leaves were cannabis, but I decided I needed to be sure, both for my own personal satisfaction and to ensure I'd not made a mistake! I carefully moistened the foliage until it was rehydrated and more flexible. After about an hour of careful teasing out and coaxing, I had three or four partially intact leaves. I then gently pressed and dried the leaves for a couple of days so at that they would retain their new position and were photographable. In most cases I would compare the leaf material with reference material from a collection but cannabis foliage is so distinctive it's not really necessary!

As an aside, current government regulations require museums to have licences to hold restricted substances. In itself, this is fine, but the application of the rules is rather ridiculous. Despite repeatedly telling the Home Office that no one in their right mind would attempt to smoke our dope, they still require the specimens be locked in separate cabinets (they are already in a locked facility) and each year the material must be weighed to see that no one has made off with some of it. Why would anyone bother to smoke it? After all, the specimens are glued to the paper. Either you'd have to role a joint with a whole herbarium sheet or scrape off the leaves from the paper. On top of that, most of the NHM plant specimens, like other museum collections, are contaminated with naphthalene or mercuric chloride and are over a hundred years old. There's not much tetrahydrocannabinol left.

The FSS herbarium is now safely ensconced in the British and Irish Herbarium of the Natural History Museum. In 2010, shortly after the collection was rescued, the government announced that it was closing the FSS. It was making a financial loss of about £2 million a month. By coincidence, one of the people I knew from 'down the pub' was a senior member of staff at the FSS. It was his dream job, or so he thought, until he was told to make everyone redundant, including himself. My friend endeavoured to prepare the staff for their redundancy and help them secure their futures and their careers. Some went abroad, some started working in the private sector and others left the profession. At the same time, the FSS had to repatriate millions of exhibits to police forces across the country. As you can imagine, the forces were not given any additional help to accommodate this influx.

Overall, forensics in this country is not in a good way. The private sector rapidly expanded following the closure of the FSS in 2010. The private companies often have specific skills or areas of expertise that they promote. Some are largely focused on human DNA work. Other companies specialise in trace evidence such as fibres or gun-shot residue. Some of the larger companies have a wider scope and take in the identification of bones, geographic information systems (GIS), archaeology and environmental forensics. In many cases, these are skills that were once found within the FSS or some police forces. More recently, parts of the private sector appear to be contracting and facing severe challenges, mainly owing to the very significant cuts that have affected police budgets over the last decade. Early in 2019, the House of Lords Science and Technology Committee completed their inquiry into the state of forensic science in England and Wales. Many of the people going before the committee expressed significant concerns, and some did not feel that the current situation is sustainable. The published report was damning – 'The evidence we received points to failings in the use of forensic science in the criminal justice system and these can be attributed to an absence of high-level leadership, a lack of funding and an insufficient level of research and development. Throughout this inquiry we heard about the decline in forensic science in England and Wales, especially since the abolition of the Forensic Science Service.'. There is widespread concern about the significant decline in the quality of forensics in England and Wales. Addressing the committee, the President of the International Association of Forensic Sciences, Professor Claude Roux, said 'When I was a student, England and Wales held, essentially, the international benchmark. It was the 'Mecca' for forensic science. Some 30 years later, my observation from the outside ... is that it has been an ongoing national crisis and, at this stage, is more of an example not to follow.'. There is also widespread concern within the criminal justice system about the ease with which unscrupulous or foolhardy people can be accepted as expert witnesses. Many feel that there are insufficient mechanisms for ensuring that potential expert witnesses are suitably qualified or experienced and that they understand and observe their duties to the court.

Personally, I feel that the police are less and less willing to try what are, to some of them, novel procedures. Not only do they appear less willing to expend on areas such as forensic botany, they also don't seem to have the time to learn about what can be achieved. Over the last three years I have offered to visit several forces to provide CSMs and detectives with information on what 'flowers' can do for them. Disappointingly, I have not had my offer taken up so far. I don't think this is hostility to the idea; sadly, I don't think they have the time. They barely have time to think, let alone plan. I can see it in their eyes. They take my business card, express enthusiasm for the idea of a seminar session and then the encroaching horror of several thousand emails stifles their minds and my card lies forgotten.

Despite the short-term gloom, I do feel that environmental forensics can improve the outcomes of criminal investigations. Forensic botany and some other areas of environmental forensics have yet to fully embrace sequencing is often confused with DNA fingerprinting (also called profiling). Sequencing is identifying the individual building blocks of our DNA, the nucleotides, while fingerprinting aggregates blocks of nucleotide code. Fingerprinting is rather like describing the make-up of a very, very long street by giving house numbers and noting whether each property is modern, Victorian or Georgian. Sequencing is rather like taking each house apart and documenting each block of stonework or brick.

Over the last few years, the technologies used in DNA sequencing have advanced considerably. Not only are we able to retrieve more data, we're are able to do it more quickly and more cheaply. Importantly, our ability to retrieve DNA from badly degraded or mixed samples has improved vastly. The advances in the retrieval of ancient DNA offer great potential for revisiting 'cold cases' and examining exhibits for traces of non-human DNA. Ancient DNA is simply the DNA that remains on old and degraded biological material. The technologies used to retrieve it were largely driven by the desire to extract DNA from extinct organisms and subfossils. For example, in the world of botany these technologies have been used to extract DNA from 300-year-old herbarium specimens to help understand the domestication of sweet potato (*Ipomoea batatas*). For those of you who are gardeners, you may recognise the name *Ipomoea*, since it's the genus to which morning glory belongs. We are now able to extract DNA from the surfaces of walls, shoes, soil or almost anything that has come into contact with biological material.

The discipline which has become known as environmental DNA (eDNA) largely has its roots in the work of conservationists and people aiming to control the spread of invasive species. One of my favourite examples of this work is a project in the Great Lakes region of North America. The Great Lakes are under serious threat: amongst other things, they are being damaged by pollution and invasive species. One introduced fish species, the sea lamprey (*Petromyzon marinus*), has been causing significant damage to fish stocks in the lakes since the first half of the twentieth century. Control of the sea lamprey has traditionally been carried out by poisoning with lampricides. Unfortunately, these chemical also harm the non-invasive lamprey species that are found in the lakes, as well as affecting other fish, such as sturgeon, and amphibians. Researchers from the University of Manitoba have recently developed a way of isolating sea lamprey DNA from river or lake water. How is this done? By tracing their wee. All animals must excrete waste, which is removed by urination or defecation. In among those waste products are cells from the animal's body. The test the scientist developed is not only able to detect sea lampreys, it is also able to tell their DNA apart from that of non-invasive lampreys living in the region. Knowing where the invasive sea lampreys are means that less environmentally impactful control measures, such as sex pheromone traps, can be used to control their population.

Using plant-DNA-based information in criminal investigations has been done. I'm not aware of any cases in the UK, but DNA fingerprinting of plants has been used in the Netherlands and in the US. Plants, like animals, rely on DNA to encode the fundamental chemistry that makes each one of us unique. However, there are exceptions. In the botanical world many plants are clonal, which means they have the same genetic make-up as each other. A typical example is the strawberry: each parent plant produces new plants by growing runners that sprout plantlets at their tips. Each one of these 'daughter' plants will be identical to the original plant. A common house-plant, the spider plant (*Chlorophytum comosum*), does the same thing: each plant has identical plantlets hanging from the ends of their floppy stems. Some naturally occurring clones can be huge; a clone of the quaking aspen (*Populus tremuloides*) in the Fishlake National Park in Utah, USA, covers 43 hectares (106 acres) and is estimated to weigh over 6,000 tons. This clone, known as 'Pando', has been estimated to be 80,000 years old. Clonality also occurs in animals. It is rarer but has been reported in some snakes, sharks and many invertebrates such as aphids.

Genetically identical plants pose a problem for forensic botany. It is unlikely that an expert witness will be able to demonstrate to the court that a suspect was at a crime scene if it is known that identical versions of the plant are found in surrounding locations and further afield. Luckily, many plants are not clonal, and plant-based DNA has been used in the courts. In Arizona, USA, the fruit of the blue palo verde tree (*Cercidium floridum*) collected from the back of a truck in which a murder victim had been transported, helped link the suspect to the crime scene. Using plant DNA, scientists were able to demonstrate that the fruit originated from a tree in the grounds of a factory where the suspect, Mark Bogan, was believed to have dumped the body of his victim, Denise Johnson. Bogan was subsequently found guilty of the murder. This 1992 case is notable as it was probably the first occasion that plant-DNA-based evidence was used in court. Such evidence remains very rare in criminal courts. The strongest barrier to it being used more widely is financial. Historically, DNA-based work has been very expensive. Thankfully, with new technologies, costs are falling, and I believe it won't be long before these techniques are more widely available.

The ability to identify a single species from an environmental sample can be turned on its head. Technically, it is now possible to build a comprehensive profile of the organisms present in a sample. It is quite amazing how many organisms are living under our noses in the most apparently inhospitable environments. A few year ago, the Natural History Museum launched a citizen science project called Microverse to investigate the microbial diversity of walls and hard surfaces in the built environment. The results astounded them; the abundance and diversity of microorganisms such as bacteria and fungi were far greater than anticipated. On top of that, the researchers found that they were able to separate microbial communities from different types of habitat. Those living on brick were different from those living on concrete, and the microbial communities found on older walls were not the same as those living on newly built properties. We are now in a position where we may be able to use those findings to identify where a suspect has been and provide robust evidence of that.

So, what's stopping us? Again, it's basically money. Before science such as this can be used in the courtroom there needs to be a lot of work. In the first instance, the core techniques need to be refined through a structured research programme. Further work includes developing cost-effective means of applying the science in the forensic environment, training CSMs and detectives, and ensuring that the approach is acceptable within the court system. This may seem like a lot of hard work but, as criminals become more aware of what 'not to do', there is a need for new and increasingly sophisticated tools to ensure the guilty are caught.

I've often enthused about the fungal organisms of this planet at various points throughout this book, which isn't surprising, considering my doctorate was on the evolution of some of these fascinating organisms. Appreciating the diverse ways microbes and fungi interact with us after we are dead is key to exploring the application of this knowledge in the forensic environment. One of my favourite groups of fungi are the Onygenales. Onygenalean fungi are particularly good at breaking down keratin, the complex protein that provides substance to the outer layer of the skin as well as hair, horns, claws and hooves. They are very specialised. Some are very familiar, such as the unpleasant athlete's foot (*Trichophyton rubrum*) or ringworm (caused by several different species). Some are important causes of human diseases. Others are more esoteric and have very particular requirements. One species, the horn stalkball (*Onygena equina*), lives on the horns and hooves of sheep, goats and horses. If you are lucky and very observant, you may find horn stalkball growing on the remains of dead animals on a country walk. Understanding how, and how fast, fungi such as the horn stalkball colonise mammalian skin, nails and hair would not only be fascinating, but it could offer important insights for forensics. If we can estimate how long a fungus has been growing, we may be able to estimate how long a person's remains have been where they were discovered.

At several points during my career in forensics I have been asked to examine fungi growing on the skin of the dead. The first case involved an infant. In fact, this was my very first case, long before I attended the suspected crime scene I described at the start of this book. I was sent pictures and asked whether it would be possible to estimate how long the child had been dead based on the growth of the fungal colonies on their skin. I found this very challenging. The pictures were graphic, the first of this nature that I had encountered. More importantly, very little is known about the types of fungi that colonise our skin after death. It was possible that the fungi might have been one of the organisms causing athlete's foot or ringworm, or it might have been something else entirely.

I advised the police that I would need a live sample of the fungus, first to identify it and then to find out how to grow it. Culturing fungi can be extremely difficult. Many have very complex and specific nutritional requirements and can be very picky feeders. The trick is to emulate their preferred food source. In this case I was planning to use one of the standard meat broth agar media. Agar media are used by biologists for growing fungi and bacteria. The media is made by cooking a broth of nutrients, such as boiled bones, and agar. On cooling, the broth sets into a firm gel upon which the fungus or bacterium can be grown. The reason the broth sets into a gel is because of the agar, which is extracted from algae, usually *Gelidium* spp. The meat provides the core nutritional needs of the fungus and the agar provides a physical base on which to grow the fungus. You may find this surprising, but microbiologists often have their own preferred recipes for the cultivating of fungi and bacteria. When I was doing my laboratory work for my PhD on *Peronosporomycetes* (yes, that word again) I used to grow my fungi on cannabis seed, termite wings or the skin scales of snakes. Cultivating the fungus from the exhibit would be essential, because without a live fungus to experiment on, I would be unable to estimate the growth rate. I was assured that a sample had been collected and would be sent immediately. After two weeks, nothing had arrived, so I contacted the police who informed me that they had lost (or damaged) the sample!

Clearly, losing evidence is very poor conduct. But this tale also leads me to another observation. In my experience, there is very little knowledge in some police forces or forensic service providers about how to correctly store living material or preserved biological specimens. On the occasions I have been asked to examine fungal colonies growing on the dead it has been evident that the fungus was stored poorly and was very likely to be dead. This is unfortunate, because it is likely that fungal and bacterial colonisation of skin surfaces may be useful in determining how long someone's remains have been in a specific environment. Consider this hypothetical situation:

a person is killed in a building, and is then stored for several days in that building before being moved to a convenient location in woodland. Being able to provide separate estimates of the post-mortem interval and the duration of that person's remains having been in that woodland could be vital in understanding how the crime was committed.

Estimating the time of death is notoriously challenging, and it is often essential to understanding the crime and securing a conviction. The provision of these estimates is often based upon the stages of decomposition as traditionally defined during the post-mortem. The people examining the remains will look for features such as body cooling, lividity, the presence of feeding insects such as blowflies and, in later stages, putrefaction. Increasingly, these observations are also being supported by the work of forensic entomologists like the team at the Natural History Museum, as well as other specialists.

For most of us decomposition is a horrible thought. It triggers alarm bells in our minds about the risk of infection and robustly reminds us of our mortality. Nearly every horror novel or film will have decomposition as a stock means of triggering fear. But decomposition is a complex and amazing biological process. As we decay, different communities of bacteria and other microbes compete for space and food. In ecology, this idea of transition is called 'succession'. Succession can be seen everywhere in the natural world. For those of you who are gardeners, colonisation of your freshly dug flower beds is an early successional stage. Leave things long enough and annual weeds will give way to perennial one, which in turn will largely be replaced by shrubs and then trees.

Decomposition is a very similar process to succession in the wider environment. Early successional stage microbes will compete for the most easily acquired food sources, the simple sugars and carbohydrates that pervade our bodies. As more and more of us is consumed, the microbes that are able to process complex compounds, such as the proteins in our ligaments and cartilage, will become ascendant. Those that consumed the simple sugars and carbohydrates will diminish and fade away and they too die. Finally, we are bones. Yet even these are home to organisms that have evolved to digest the tough composition of our skeleton. Bacteria and fungi are amazingly diverse and many of them are extremely specialised.

The complexity and diversity of the microbial world is increasingly being explored with the aim of furthering our understanding of the post-mortem interval. The increasing awareness that decomposition is successional and therefore chronological has opened up the world of the decay-causing organisms as a means of better estimating the post-mortem interval. Recent technological advances in sequencing DNA have made retrieving data practical and faster. Importantly, the advent of relatively cheap DNA sequencing has made it more affordable for scientists to explore these complex communities of organisms. Detailed study of the biology of decomposition is so recent – most of the work having been done since 2010 – that there are two alternative terms used to describe it. Both 'Necrobiome' and 'thanatomicrobiome' appeared in the scientific literature at roughly the same time, although the former appears to be the more widely used term. They both describe the communities of microbes found on and within us after our death. These microbes are an essential component of the decomposition process

The number of scientific publications in this area is still small but some conclusions are emerging. The primary external factor that significantly alters the rate of internal decomposition is temperature, although water and humidity may also have some impact. If we can establish the average temperatures of a wood where a body has been lying, potentially we have the means to estimate how long someone has been dead. Research using DNA sequence data has shown that the microbial community within the body changes significantly during decomposition. For example, the abundance of the members of the bacterial genus *Clostridium* increases as the body decays. This is also one of the reasons poorly stored meat is potentially dangerous: *Clostridium* bacteria produce several compounds that are highly toxic to humans. There is also a point where the rupturing of the body releases nutrients into the adjoining environment and increases the pH of that environment. We are probably a few years away from a 'microbial clock' being used as evidence in court, but I believe the approach will become standard before too long.

The microbial clock within our bodies is reflected in the responses of the living communities that surround us after death. I quite often hear people suggest that it is possible to detect a clandestine burial by the increased growth of the plants above or nearby. Unfortunately, reality is far more complex than that relatively simple proposition. Around the world, several scientific studies using experimental grave plots containing either pig carcasses or empty placebo graves have been done. In many instances of both cases, the plants respond to disturbance of the ground and grow more vigorously. The most likely cause for this is probably the release and mobilisation of soil nutrients caused by the act of digging a hole and disturbing the soil structure. This is comparable to the process of cultivation in gardening or agriculture.

If roots are unable to reach the body and the immediate area surrounding it, deeper burials are unlikely to affect the growth of the plants. Plants gain nutrients in a very different way to animals. Simply put, plants take sunlight energy, carbon dioxide and water and build carbohydrates such as sugars. They gain energy, via sunlight, by building simple molecules into more complex ones. Animals survive by doing the opposite, we take complex organic compounds and break them down into simpler compounds. The early stages of decomposition result in the production by bacteria of breakdown compounds, of which many are quite complex and probably toxic to plant growth. It is only during the latest stages of decomposition that the breakdown compounds become available for plants to metabolise. In most circumstances, it is probable that at first the presence of a dead body inhibits plants growth, but as time progresses, there may be an increase in growth. The complexity of this system is increased when we consider the potential impacts of soil type or other organisms such as fungi and invertebrates in the ecosystem. The whole topic is deeply fascinating and requires considerable research. Ideally, to do this there is a need for a body farm to be set up in this country so that the environmental and ecological interactions upon the dead can be properly studied here. Body farms are places where scientists can study the processes of decomposition upon the human body. People donate their own bodies with the aim of supporting important scientific research into what happens to us after death. The farms particularly aim to emulate murder or disaster scenarios. Probably the most famous body farm in the world is the one in Tennessee. There are now facilities in several locations across the USA, Australia and the Netherlands. Hopefully, we will establish one in the UK as well. Body farms are valuable for understanding how causes of death such as traumatic injury or drowning are affected by decay. They are also valuable for understanding how the necrobiome develops. While scientists can do experiments on donated human tissue in laboratories or on proxies such as pigs, they are a poor substitute. It is important to be able to work with the donated remains of people. Thankfully, a growing appreciation of the value of this work means that many people are willing to donate themselves after their demise. I have a feeling I may consider this. I have always fancied the idea of a sky burial, where our remains are placed in the open so that wild scavengers can feed upon us. In some parts of the world this role is performed by vultures. Sadly, in many regions, vultures are now critically endangered owing to diclofenac poisoning (diclofenac is used in veterinary practices as a painkiller); the vultures are killed by the diclofenac-impregnated carcasses of domestic animals. In some species, over 95% of the vultures have been eradicated with serious environmental and human health consequences. Fewer vultures means that more carcasses are left for jackals, foxes and feral dogs to feed off; and because of the resultant increase in their populations there has been a rise in the number of rabies cases in some areas. Clearly, there are no vultures in southern England, but perhaps a nice farmer will lay me out so that I can feed the local red kite population. I'd like that.

The future of environmental forensics looks promising and exciting, but only if we can overcome the very significant public and research finance challenges that prevail. The recent advances in environmental DNA and ancient DNA technologies have the potential to revolutionise how crime scenes are managed. Exploring how the microbial community alters our remains after death through the gradually expanding international research community of body farms is very likely to help investigators improve their estimation of time of death. All these advances, when supported with robust and consistent exhibit collection and documentation, have the potential to place environmental forensics at the heart of thoroughly presented and verifiable evidence in court. These novel approaches must be developed alongside traditional skills based upon the ability to identify plants (and other organisms) in a crime scene and the understanding of how they may be evidentially relevant.

My time in the world of forensic botany continues to be unexpected and fascinating. Our planet is full of amazing life, and the plants we walk by nourish and enrich our lives. I'm very lucky that I can wander down the road, enjoying the diversity of plants around me, open the gate to my allotment and sit at ease in my greenhouse. Within my greenhouse, I can contemplate the latest batch of seed I have germinated. This year, I'm particularly chuffed with the five varieties of tomato I am growing, and in a week or so, I'll be able to eat the first ones, fresh off the vine some forty-eight years after my father left the ones from the sewage plant on the kitchen table.

It is an honour to be able to use my knowledge to help seek justice for those whose lives are prematurely shortened because of the actions of others. My knowledge has evolved over decades watching and wondering, often with the love and support of family and friends. By the time I was twelve, my mother had become expert at the emergency stop while driving. Sat in the front passenger's seat, gazing out of the window, I'd suddenly let out a shriek, calmly she'd say 'where?' and excitedly I'd say, 'back twenty yards'. Mum would then reverse the required distance and I'd leap out and jump into the ditch. This was how I first saw meadow crane's-bill (*Geranium pratense*), one of our most beautiful wild plants. Entering the world of forensic botany has reinvigorated and enriched my relationship with plants. Not only do I now spend a lot more time paying them intimate attention down a microscope, I also look at them differently. I'll often find myself musing on the growth forms of plants, how the branches relate to one another, or how they might regrow after being damaged when people commit crimes. I am acknowledging that after well over forty-five years of gazing at plants, I still have a huge amount to learn.

Finally, I have the greatest admiration for those who work tirelessly, every day of the week, for many years at a time, trying to solve serious crimes and gain justice for the victims and their families and friends. They deserve our gratitude. But most of all, I will remember the dead. They have changed my life.

Acknowledgements

I wish to thank my forensic anthropologist colleague and friend 'Sophie', she has been incredibly important to me in guiding me along this bramble strewn, muddy dark path. The work that forensic specialists and police force staff do is immensely tough; anyone who can work on serious crime cases such as murder and remain composed deserves our respect and gratitude. Standing on freezing cold roadsides with detectives, PolSAs and CSMs, I've learned a lot, a very big thanks to all of them.

To my former editor Zena Alkayat I owe special gratitude, this book would not have come to be without her. Thanks also to Susannah Otter who took up the challenge of being my editor and to Steve Burdett who gave some editorial guidance. A huge thanks to my lovely agent Douglas Keen who was brave enough to withstand the occasional rant and listened to me waffle on over a glass or two of wine. To Edward my lovely partner, I'm deeply grateful for his love and patience and very constructive criticism of various drafts. Also, my brilliant bibliophile friend Debbie for telling me that an early version of this book was 'not shit' – from her that was an accolade which spurred me on! Also, lots of love to my mum and family who are mostly too squeamish to read this book. Thanks to my former colleagues and friends at the Natural History Museum, especially Julie Gray, Dave Williams, Martin Hall and Amoret Whitaker. Thanks also to Wenbo Chen for his translation.

This work is not an academic work, and early on, I decided to anonymise most people, both living and the dead. I made some exceptions to this rule when discussing well publicised cases that I had not participated in. Consequently, I have not mentioned many of the brilliant scientists whose work has contributed to the development of environmental forensics. In reparation for this omission. and as a means of allowing the more curious reader to learn more, I have provided a brief reading list.

Reading List

David O. Carter, Jeffery K. Tomberlin, M. Eric Benbow and Jessica L. Metcalf (eds.) (2017) *Forensic Microbiology (Forensic Science in Focus)*

David W. Hall and Jason Byrd (2012) *Forensic Botany: A Practical Guide (Essential Forensic Science).*

Stuart H. James, Jon J. Nordby and Suzanne Bell (2014) *Forensic Science: An Introduction to Scientific and Investigative Techniques*

Julie Roberts and Nicholas Márquez–Grant (2012) *Forensic Ecology Handbook: From Crime Scene to Court (Developments in Forensic Science)*

Patricia Wiltshire (2019) *Traces: The memoir of a forensic scientist and criminal investigator*